Perspective on the Nature of Geography

The Monograph Series
of the Association of American Geographers

PERSPECTIVE ON THE NATURE OF GEOGRAPHY
Richard Hartshorne

ON THE MARGINS OF THE GOOD EARTH
D. W. Meinig

OFFSHORE GEOGRAPHY OF NORTHWESTERN EUROPE
Lewis M. Alexander

Perspective on

the Nature of Geography

RICHARD HARTSHORNE

London
JOHN MURRAY
50 Albemarle Street, W.1

First published in Great Britain 1960
Fifth impression 1966

Copyright © 1959 by The Association of American Geographers
Printed in Great Britain
by Butler & Tanner Ltd
Frome and London

CONTENTS

PREFACE   vii

I. *Foreword—The Need and Purpose*   1

II. *What Is Meant by Geography
as the Study of Areal Differentiation?*   12

III. *What Is Meant by the "Earth Surface"?*   22

IV. *Is the Integration of Heterogeneous Phenomena
a Peculiarity of Geography?*   26

V. *What Is the Measure of "Significance"
in Geography?*   36

VI. *Must We Distinguish Between Human and
Natural Factors?*   48

VII. *The Division of Geography by Topical Fields—
The Dualism of Physical and Human Geography*   65

VIII. *Time and Genesis in Geography*   81

IX. *Is Geography Divided Between "Systematic"
and "Regional" Geography?*   108

X. *Does Geography Seek to Formulate
Scientific Laws or to Describe Individual Cases?*   146

XI. *The Place of Geography in a Classification
of the Sciences*   173

XII. *Afterword*   183

REFERENCES   185

AUTHOR INDEX   195

SUBJECT INDEX   198

EDITOR'S NOTE

The circumstances under which this manuscript came to me are indicated in the Preface of the editorial selection board. I can only add that the subsequent experience of working with the author has been thoroughly enjoyable. I am convinced that the work is a most timely contribution to the literature of geographical methodology and that we are all very much in Professor Hartshorne's debt for it. If the reader gets from it but a fraction of the insights and stimulus which, even in occasional disagreement, were my good fortune to acquire, he will be well rewarded. Moreover, I can affirm strongly the judgment of the editorial board that the author has no intent to lay out an undeviating course which all geographers should follow. But the book does ask that geographers work purposefully and think clearly about what they are doing in our great co-operative effort to advance knowledge of the world in which we live. To such a request there surely must be a wholehearted and unanimous affirmative response.

ANDREW H. CLARK
Madison, Wisconsin

PREFACE

FOR TWENTY YEARS THE LEADING methodological treatment of geography in English has been Richard Hartshorne's *The Nature of Geography*. First published in 1939 in two expanded numbers of the *Annals* of the Association of American Geographers and reprinted at the time in book form, it has often been reissued by photo-offset. In 1946 the author made some minor revisions and additions which were presented as notes on added pages without alteration of the original text, and these have been included in all subsequent reprintings.

Meanwhile, more and more persons have become geographers, and the literature of substantive geographical research has grown enormously. At the same time, geographers in all countries have continued to study the history of geographical thought, to undertake new analyses of geographical methodology, and to suggest further avenues for exploration along these lines. Hence, under circumstances described in his Foreword, Professor Hartshorne was moved to make a new statement which would bring up to date his own and others' thinking, and would express a logical concept of geographic investigation and scholarship more directly and in a more affirmative manner than in the earlier work.

The study was completed in first draft at the time the Monograph Series was announced. It was submitted to the first editor of the series, Derwent Whittlesey, shortly before his untimely death, and came thereafter to the present editor, Andrew H. Clark. Because of his personal association with the author as a colleague, and because he had been among those who had urged the author to write such a positive statement, Professor Clark withdrew from the selection board and was replaced by Edward A. Ackerman, who served with the other undersigned regular members at the time. This board recommended the work for publication.

Naturally, neither all members of the original board nor the editor are in complete agreement with every statement made by the author, but all are agreed that the book is fresh, challenging, vigorous, and consistent, and that no careful reader can fail to be indebted to the author for his painstaking search through the literature of geographic methodology and for his brilliant, coherent reasoning.

As Professor Hartshorne himself points out, we can advance geography only by doing it and not by merely talking about the "hows" and "whys." Yet geographers cannot—nor should they—leave the methodological theme alone. Again and again in inaugural lectures, presidential addresses, or elsewhere, out of the individual scholar's urge to justify his own work, the statements pour forth. So many and often so sharply conflicting are the views set forth that the casual geographer, the neophyte, or the visitor from a neighboring field may well be confused. This book is an attempt to resolve some of the confusion. Obviously no one expects it to put an end to more than a century of logical disputation.

No methodology is ever complete, nor should any scholar or society of scholars seek to prescribe the bounds or orientation of interests shared with thousands. Therefore, to read this volume as a set of final conclusions would be contrary to the purpose both of the author and of the Association which has sponsored its publication. By setting forth, however, the matured conclusions of a man given to thinking deeply about the methodological problems of his field and widely familiar with the writings of others who have discussed such problems, this study should stimulate its readers to think more clearly on the nature of geographical investigation and give encouragement and an intellectual "lift" to geographers in quest of a better understanding of what they are doing and why.

EDWARD A. ACKERMAN
F. KENNETH HARE
GILBERT F. WHITE
JOHN K. WRIGHT

I.

Foreword — The Need and Purpose

GEOGRAPHY in the past two decades has experienced a marked expansion in universities in English-speaking countries. With this expansion there has been an increased interest in fundamental questions concerning the nature and purpose of geography as a field of higher learning.

For the most part these questions are not new. The views of scores of geographers concerning them were published in 1939 in *The Nature of Geography.*[1] But the encyclopedic character of that work and the large amount of attention devoted to negative criticism, though essential in both cases to the purpose of the study, tend to obscure its positive conclusions. The criticisms and challenges that have been raised since then, in the literature, in

[1] Richard Hartshorne, *The Nature of Geography*, published originally in the *Annals* of the Association of American Geographers, Vol. XXIX (1939), and subsequently republished by the Association in book form in numerous printings. Because the questions considered in this study were discussed in the previous work, with specific references to some three hundred methodological studies, that work is used here as a convenient collection of sources which has been found to be reliable. A citation to that work in this study refers, in most cases, not to my views but to those of other writers, in some cases many others, which are quoted or paraphrased in the earlier work. Page citations refer to numbers at the bottom of the page; these are identical in all editions except that pages in Roman numerals appear only in the editions published since 1946. Citations in the present work are given in square brackets; the first number refers to the work cited, as listed at the end of the volume, the following numbers to the specific pages.

correspondence, and in seminar discussions, have demonstrated the need for a reconsideration of ten basic questions,[2] each of which forms the topic of a chapter in this book.

For some of these questions the methodological studies published since 1939 support the conclusions presented in *The Nature of Geography,* which are therefore restated in this book only briefly, but, I hope, more clearly. In other cases the development of geographic thought in the subsequent period of nearly twenty years has made substantial revision necessary.

It is not the purpose of this study, however, merely to add fuel to what more than one writer has bewailed as "endless methodological discussion." Fruitless repetition of argument can best be avoided by careful examination of what others have written, seeking to establish the points of agreement, and to base disagreement on understanding and correct representation of views subjected to criticism.

The history of methodological discussion in German geography indicates the value of this procedure. Since the latter part of the nineteenth century, German writers have engaged in vigorous debate over methodological issues in published studies which provide the reader with full representation of opposing views and enable him readily to find the materials used in evidence. Richthofen's programmatic address of 1883 could win general acceptance, in part because the issues he considered had previously been debated in a series of conflicting papers, which were considered critically in Wagner's periodic reviews in the *Geographisches Jahrbuch.*

[2] Several of these questions were brought forcefully to the attention of the profession in 1953 in the posthumous publication of Schaefer's examination of "Exceptionalism in Geography" [*116*]. The reply which I made in 1955 was limited to consideration of errors in that examination, primarily in reference to the writings of Kant, Humboldt, Ritter, Hettner, and myself [*104*]. On the urging of several colleagues, I also agreed to prepare a second paper for the *Annals* of the Association of American Geographers which should deal constructively with the methodological questions which were raised in the critique but which, independently thereof, had been troubling many geographers [*104*:205f.]. Since the resultant study developed far beyond the length of a normal paper for the *Annals,* the editor of that journal suggested that it be published as a separate monograph. The opportunity to publish it in the new series sponsored by the Association has made it possible to give more thorough consideration to the questions at issue.

Thanks to the continued discussions by the following generation, notably in the work of Hettner,[3] German geographers came
to a greater degree of mutual understanding and agreement over
the basic concepts of the field than appears to be the case in any
other country [*1*:91–101].[4] Commenting on this fact in his address
on "Degrees of Freedom," Manley suggests that it may be due to
a willingness of Germans to accept discipline in contrast to British concern for freedom in research [*81*:21ff.]. Plausible as this explanation may seem, quite the opposite is indicated by the actual
character of methodological discussion in the German literature.
If these show any effort to assert discipline, it is an insistence that
writers on these questions should first read what others have written [*1*:27, 34, 138].

With general agreement on fundamental issues, German geographers maintain a vigorous and scholarly examination of other
methodological questions. Many of these discussions, however, are
somewhat difficult to follow, at least for the foreign reader, because of the ambiguity of meaning of the term *"Landschaft."* If,
as several writers assert, the present generation of German geographers is in agreement that this concept is close to the heart or
core of geography, there appears to be no more agreement on
what the term means than was the case when I expressed bewild-
erment twenty years ago [*1*:149–58].[5]

These difficulties are multiplied in discussion between Ger-
man- and English-speaking geographers when the words *"Landschaft"* and "landscape" are treated as synonymous. Confusion resulted in the first instance when the German term, which can
mean either "scene" or "region," was introduced into American
and British geography simply as "landscape." In the effort to as-
sure clarity of thought on our side, *The Nature of Geography* of-

---

[3] Heinrich Schmitthenner provides a detailed sketch of Hettner's professional
background and career, included in the posthumous publication of Alfred
Hettner, *Allgemeine Geographie des Menschen,* Band I, Stuttgart, 1947,
pp. xi–xxxiv.

[4] On the method of noting citations in the brackets, see footnote 1 on page 1.

[5] Lautensach, writing in 1953, accepts that criticism as understatement. Examining the writings of his colleagues, he found not only that the term was used
in different meanings by different writers but that in certain cases it was used
in the same article in four, or even as many as eight, meanings without mention of change in meaning [*37*:14f.].

fered a definition of "landscape" consistent with the common meaning of the word in English but independent of the German word [*1*:158–90]. But when German writers assume that that definition of "landscape" was intended as a definition of *Landschaft*, the confusion is worse confounded.[6]

In France recent methodological studies likewise demonstrate the value of critical scholarship, although the lack of full documentation in many cases lessens the usefulness of the studies, at least for readers not familiar with the previous work in the French literature. Insofar as one can judge from references, however, French geographers appear to restrict their study of methodology to their own literature. While they look to Humboldt and Ritter as having laid the foundations of modern geography, and to Ratzel as the leader in establishing human geography [*19*; *55*:26; *59*:14f.], they rarely refer to the methodological views of later foreign writers.[7] A recent paper by Hamelin of Quebec (if we may include it in the French literature for the purpose of this discussion) does draw extensively from methodological studies in both French and English [*57*].

British geographers, it was noted two decades ago, have shown much less interest than those of other countries in seeking to determine the nature and scope of their field [*1*:100]. The addition of new chairs of geography in many more universities in recent years, however, has impelled many to stand up and assert a position. Discussions of the purpose and scope of geography have appeared recently in one or more books, in a number of articles, and especially in numerous inaugural addresses of students appointed to professorships of geography both in Great Britain and in other countries of the Commonwealth. In general, in English-

---

[6] While we could avoid this danger if, as has been suggested, English-speaking geographers would accept the double meaning for our word which German usage permits in their case, this would only mean that we would be in agreement in common misunderstanding of what we were writing. Fortunately, there are limits on our freedom to change the meaning of common words.

[7] Recognizing a similar situation in British geography, Manley's "Degrees of Freedom" speaks with favor of "provincial traditions" in geography [*81*]. Certainly we can welcome a healthy variety in the character of geographic work, but we are not free to be ignorant of knowledge and ideas that are readily available. In that sense of the word, as Manley surely would agree, there is no place for a provincial attitude in geography.

speaking countries, including the United States, it has been traditional for geographers to discuss methodological problems primarily in papers prepared as oral addresses rather than as research studies. To the extent that these present ideas developed in the course of a long-range research program or suggestions for new problems for research, a reader may accept what appears to him of value and ignore what does not. In many cases, however, such papers include discussion of long-standing problems with little consideration of the studies of those problems which have been made by earlier scholars. As a result of this practice, and particularly of the lack of references or bibliography in many methodological papers by British geographers, valuable material is soon eclipsed and left buried in the literature [*1*:xxvii].

Thus Herbertson's posthumous paper of 1915 [*7*], though pertinent to current discussions, as we will find, is seldom if ever mentioned by British geographers [*1*:xxxi]. Even more notable is the case of Mackinder's "famous revolutionary paper" of 1887 on "The Scope and Methods of Geography" [*16*]. I find no reference to the views expressed in that paper in the methodological literature of the present century prior to Unstead's survey in 1949 of Mackinder's contributions to geography [*90*] and the republication of the paper itself in 1951 by the Royal Geographical Society. For example, in Wooldridge's volume of his methodological addresses of the decade 1945–54, this paper, which he rightly calls "the founding document of British geography," is drawn upon only in his Introduction, dated 1956 [*92*:2f.], in which he also expresses surprise that the paper was not included in the bibliography of *The Nature of Geography,* where indeed it certainly should have been included.

Much of the methodological discussion of British and American geographers has the character of literary essays rather than of scholarly studies. This is appropriate when the purpose is to present a viewpoint derived from a writer's own thought and experience or to stimulate other students to work in particular directions which the writer believes will be most valuable. But when the discussion involves consideration of the ideas of previous writers, or of the historical development of geographic thought, the reader may properly expect that the writing will demonstrate scholarly research [*102*:116–18]. This is frequently lacking. Even in what purports to be presentation of historical or bibliographical information, the judgments or conjectures of the writer are often not distinguished from facts verifiable in the printed record. When a paper is documented with numerous references, the reader may not notice whether its more significant statements carry specific references; he is almost certain to be deceived when such references are supplied but do not in fact substantiate the statements to which they are attached.

Methodological problems are frequently discussed in both America and Britain without study of the findings of previous students of the same problems [cf. Wooldridge, *92*:20]. To a much greater extent than in substantive studies, the literature in foreign languages is ignored, save for what has appeared in translation. Frequently such material is used without reference, or with reference only to the original, although the phrasing demonstrates dependence on an unnamed secondary source.

When the conclusions found in other studies are considered and criticized, they are often presented in inadequate or misleading paraphrases, with or without specific citations. It is, of course, difficult to avoid errors in paraphrasing even when working with care. The use of obviously "watered down" or "slanted" phrasing is evidence to the critical reader of carelessness. But, in the absence of such evidence, the reader may not realize that an adverse judgment by a critic of statements presented in paraphrase is based not on what the original student actually wrote but rather on the impression which that made on the mind of the critic. In a number of cases such impressions are then used as the basis for deducing the viewpoint of the original author on questions on which he had expressed no view, or even had expressed the opposite of that which the critic deduces for him.[8]

The attitude described is understandable. Whatever views we may hold concerning the nature and scope of geography, no doubt all would agree that its purpose is to add to man's knowl-

---

[8] The critical statements of the preceding paragraphs were not derived from any manual of scholarship but from specific cases in recent methodological writings of American and British geographers, including students who adhere strictly to the rules of scholarship in their substantive works.

edge of reality. Methodology adds nothing to that knowledge, but only to our understanding of such knowledge. Hence, it is felt, time spent in research for a methodological paper is time lost from the real work of geography; the less time lost in this way, the better.

· The thesis is plausible but illusory. The individual writer may save time by ignoring the requirements for scholarly research, but geographers collectively lose much time and effort in repetitious and confusing discussion—in what Darby described, with intentional exaggeration, as "methodological babble" [*68*:9]. The failure to study carefully and transmit accurately what others actually have written leads to fruitless discussion over nonexistent disagreements, while the lack of thorough documentation hides, no doubt from the critic as well as his readers, the degree of agreement which actually exists.

The purpose of methodological writing is neither the assertion of independent opinions nor contentious argumentation, but rather the clarification of problems of mutual concern. This purpose necessarily involves logical disputation, and may require the removal of obstructions to understanding that are caused by misleading or erroneous statements. In considering the refutation of errors, both writer and reader share the responsibility to focus attention on the work under criticism rather than its author; methodological scholarship is not concerned with persons but with ideas expressed in writings [*102*:124]. This is particularly true of methodological papers by writers whose primary interest and professional standing depend not on such papers but on their substantive works. We may, however, expect both an increase in quality and a decrease in quantity of methodological studies, if writers anticipate that what they publish in this field will be subjected to critical scrutiny based on the application of rigorous standards of scholarship [*104*:207f.].

METHOD OF APPROACH

This book follows the principle on which *The Nature of Geography* was based, namely, that the determination of the nature, scope, and purpose of geography is primarily a problem in empirical research. As an established field of long historical develop-

ment, possessing a rich literature, methodological as well as substantive, geography is what geographers have made it, and in
large part it is likely to change that character but slowly [*1*:30].

A first step in *The Nature of Geography* was to seek the most
reliable description possible of geography, as seen through the
eyes of geographers of the past as well as of the present. Needless
to say, geographers never agree completely, and often disagree
radically, in defining their subject. It was necessary to determine
to what extent progressive differences represent consistent development of thought, resulting from reflective study of previous
writings and the development of methods in substantive work.
The same method was followed in seeking answers to particular
questions that have been raised concerning work in geography.[9]

This "critical examination in the light of the past" is, of
course, not automatic; it involves logical judgment, whether that
of the writers quoted or of the author himself. But the logic followed can be tested by the reader at each step: if that is sound,
the conclusions follow from the premises. If the reader questions
the conclusion, his task is to demonstrate the error in the statements of facts, or in the premises or the logical reasoning. This is
a different level of rational thought than mere difference of opin-
ion.[10]

This approach, it must be emphasized, allows free opportunity
for new ideas about geography. There is no presumption that we
must continue to work with the same basic concepts which guided
the work of our predecessors. But if we are to avoid dissipating
our efforts in ever changing directions, we must understand and
evaluate the framework for geography which has been developed
hitherto. Failure to do this has enabled promoters of novel ideas

[9] A concept presented in *The Nature of Geography* as taken from studies of
other geographers is not properly referred to simply as my view. Adequate
criticism of such a concept or viewpoint requires consideration of the recorded views of many students. For the purpose of locating such statements,
I have found it necessary and useful to make repeated use of the indexes of
authors and subjects in that work (even though the latter is incomplete, and
in both there are numerous cases in which the page number is incorrect—
usually by only plus or minus one).

[10] The above seems to be a more correct description of my role as author in
The Nature of Geography than that which I stated in the introduction, and
which many readers have questioned, namely, that my concern was merely
"to present geography as other geographers see it" [*1*:31].

repeatedly to persuade groups of geographers to pursue apparently new and attractive concepts of the subject, which ultimately prove to be distractions, producing studies which are hailed when written as landmarks, but which later we find of little use. This loss of scholarly effort appears all the more unnecessary when we find in the study of the history of geographic thought that the concepts hailed as new had been tried decades or even a century earlier and were found wanting.

Hence, with Braun and Obst, we view with skepticism proposals for changes that are presented without knowledge and consideration of past understandings and concepts recorded in the literature [1:34]. If those who propose new views of the field would first appraise the thought and work of previous students, they would not only save themselves and others much loss of time, but would be better able to promote those innovations that are sound.

Such an attitude toward the work of our predecessors engenders respect for our field and a healthy sense of modesty, which is not to be misconstrued as worship of the past. It should also enable us to recognize logical errors in our heritage of geographical thought, and to determine where our conceptual structure needs to be rectified or strengthened.

The establishment of a logically sound structure of the nature of geography will not in itself, however, provide the impetus necessary for substantial progress in geographic knowledge; neither, on the other hand, will the mere accumulation of descriptions of areas which, however detailed, remain superficial depictions of observable facts. What geography needs most today, as a critic of an early draft of this study noted, is to develop new conceptual approaches and more effective ways of measuring the interrelationships of phenomena. These will not be forthcoming, as he noted, from another restatement of the field of geography as it has evolved; neither will they result from any attempt to transform its essential character.

New conceptual approaches and techniques will result only from intensive substantive work in particular branches or aspects of the field. American geographers in the last decade or so have developed, I believe, a greater number of significant and useful concepts and methods than in any previous period. Among the many which may be listed we may mention the development of statistical tools for analysis of the market factor in industrial location and for correlating various indices of urban phenomena and combined cartographic-statistical methods of correlating presumably related phenomena. These may provide us with analytical methods that would permit a revolution in the speed and precision of determining areal correlations.

In order, however, that such new concepts and tools may be effective as an impetus to geographic scholarship, it is necessary that there be some basis of agreement in the profession concerning the nature, scope, and purpose of our work. To forward that need is the purpose of a methodological study such as this. Its concern is not to defend a position once taken, nor to project a new orientation, but rather to clarify our mutual understanding of what we have inherited.

In seeking to further such clarification, the author has been greatly assisted during the several years of preparing this study by a number of colleagues who have read portions of earlier drafts and offered valuable suggestions, by the students in successive classes of his graduate course on "The History of Geographic Thought," and, most especially, by the editor. His innumerable criticisms, of substance as well as of form, have far exceeded the normal functions of an editor and have been of great help in enabling the author to see more clearly what he had been attempting to say.

ORDER OF APPROACH

In *The Nature of Geography* the consideration of specific questions concerning the intrinsic character and purpose of geography was preceded by Hettner's statement of the logical position of geography in the total field of knowledge. This order of presentation may well have given the reader the erroneous impression that Hettner's statement constituted a basic proposition from which were derived, by logical reasoning, answers to the questions subsequently discussed.

To eliminate any appearance of deductive reasoning from a priori theories concerning either geography or science, this book will proceed inductively, seeking to determine the actual character of geographic work as geographers have viewed that work. On this basis it should be possible to determine what kind of study it is. Whether such a field is to be called "science" is a semantic question, depending on what particular definition is given to a word on which there is much disagreement. The character of geography as a field of study should be determined independently of that semantic question.

If by this means we attain clarification of the questions of fact about geography, we may then, as our final topic, consider Hettner's concept of the position of geography among the sciences, treating it as a hypothesis designed to explain the characteristics of geography previously established by empirical evidence. Such a hypothesis is in no way necessary to the consideration of the previous topics, in each of which the purpose is to establish facts concerning the character of geography, in comparison with that of other disciplines. Rather, the hypothesis is to be judged in terms of the degree to which it fits the facts as empirically determined and makes them more intelligible.

II.

What Is Meant by Geography as the
Study of Areal Differentiation?

MANY STUDENTS have found difficulty with the statement of geography as "the science of areal differentiation." The phrase "areal differentiation" was introduced by Sauer in 1925 in paraphrasing Hettner's statement of his concept of geography [24:20]. In the following years it was used by numerous American geographers as a convenient term to indicate in two words of common English origin what otherwise would require many more words to express. For the same reason it was used repeatedly in *The Nature of Geography*.

Experience, however, suggests that for many readers the term is either meaningless or misleading. Most of the objections raised concerning the concept identified by the term are directed at what the critic infers merely from his interpretation of the words in the phrase. If the critic's inference leads to conclusions that are unacceptable, he discards not merely the term, but the concept for which it stands.

The concept itself stems from Richthofen's synthesis of the views of Humboldt and Ritter [1:92], and has been most fully expounded in Hettner's writings. Whether in the form expressed by Hettner or in minor variations, it has been followed by the great majority of German geographers of the present century [1:92, 98,138; cf. Sölch, 46:147f.; and Plewe, 41:411].

Hettner expressed the concept numerous times in statements varying somewhat in form but little in meaning. Thus in 1898 he found that "the distinctive subject of geography, from the most ancient times to the present, was the knowledge of earth areas as they differ from each other" (*die Erkenntnis der Erdräume nach ihrer Verschiedenheit*), that man was included as an integral part of the nature of an area (*Landesnatur*), and that with the general advance of science "mere description has been replaced in all branches of geography by search for causes" [*9*:320; *1*:98]. In 1905 he wrote of "the chorological science of the earth or the science of earth areas and places in terms of their difference and their spatial relations" (*nach ihrer Verschiedenheit und nach ihren räumlichen Beziehungen*) or "the science of the earth surface in terms of its regional differences—i.e., as a complex of continents, lands, districts, and localities" [*11*:553; repeated, in slightly different form in 1927, *2*:122; *1*:237]. He also wrote in terms of the character of areas [*11*:561; *2*:123f; *1*:142], and his complete thought is perhaps most fully expressed in a long statement in his 1927 volume:

> The goal of the chorological point of view is to know the character of regions and places through comprehension of the existence together and interrelations among the different realms of reality and their varied manifestations, and to comprehend the earth surface as a whole in its actual arrangement in continents, larger and smaller regions, and places.[1]

Similar in meaning, though different in form and tone, are the more familiar statements of Vidal de la Blache: "Geography is the science of places," concerned with the qualities and potentialities of countries [*1*:241]. "The particular character of a country" is expressed by the totality of its features, "the social diver-

[1] "Das Ziel der chorologischen Auffassung ist die Erkenntnis des Charakters der Länder und Örtlichkeiten aus dem Verständnis des Zusammenseins und Zusammenwirkens der verschiedenen Naturreiche und ihrer verschiedenen Erscheinungsformen und die Auffassung der ganzen Erdoberfläche in ihrer natürlichen Gliederung in Erdteile, Länder, Landschaften und Örtlichkeiten" [*2*:130]. Correct translation of several of the terms involved depends on study of the context and of Hettner's usage in general.

sities associated with the diversities of places" [*1*:131]. More recently, Cholley has restated this view in his excellent *Guide to the Student of Geography*: "The object of geography is to know the earth," in its total character, not in terms of individual categories of phenomena, physical, biological, and human arranged in a series, but rather in terms of "the combinations produced among them, because it is these combinations which create the different physical and human aspects which the surface of the earth reveals to us. . . . It is an astonishing variety of aspects which this cover reveals to us: oceans, continents, and, overlying them, all the diversity of vegetational landscapes, of systems of culture, forms of settlement and the organization of area (*espace*) by the human groups" [*52*:14f.].[2]

Since the publication of *The Nature of Geography*, various writers have attempted to state the concept in English in terms that might be understood by laymen. Thus the definition of geography proposed in 1950 by the Glossary Committee of British geographers reads: "the science that describes the earth's surface with particular reference to the differentiation and relationships of areas" [*76*:158]. The editors of the *American College Dictionary*, after consulting with me on this definition, produced a much longer statement: "the study of the areal differentiation of the earth surface, as shown in the character, arrangement, and interrelations over the earth of elements such as climate, relief, soil, vegetation, population, land use, industries, or states, and of the unit areas formed by the complex of these individual elements." Preston James, writing for the Committee on American Geography, in his Introduction to *American Geography: Inventory and Prospect*, puts it more briefly: "Geography . . . deals with the associations of phenomena that give character to particular places, and with the likenesses and differences among places" [*4*:6].

None of these statements reveals the background thinking out

---

[2] Cholley's writing undoubtedly owes much to that of Vidal de la Blache. It is not possible to determine from his book whether the similarity of his viewpoint to that of Hettner and other German geographers represents independent thought or the influence of their writings, either direct or through intermediary sources.

of which it has evolved. It should further understanding of the concept to remind ourselves, in elementary terms, of the basic reasons for the existence of a field called geography. If the combination of factors found in any area of the earth—the particular conditions of climate, landforms, soils, population, crops, farms, cities, and so forth—were found to be almost the same in every other area, geography would be reduced to the problem of determining the interrelationships among these diverse factors which produced the total complex repeated without variation over the world. Under these conditions, such a subject, if it existed at all as a separate discipline, would no doubt have developed relatively late and as an over-all integrating science of little popular interest.

Very early in human development, however, man discovered that his world varied greatly from place to place. It was to satisfy man's curiosity concerning such differences that geography developed as a subject of popular interest. From earliest times travelers returning from "foreign" parts were expected to tell the stay-at-homes what things and people were like in the places they had seen, whether in adjoining, but relatively inaccessible, districts or in more remote parts.

This universal curiosity of man about the world beyond his immediate horizon, a world known to differ in varying degrees from the home area, is the foundation of all geography. Among the innumerable geographers of divers countries who have stated this principle explicitly we may mention Strabo, Vidal de la Blache, Volz, Sauer, and Darby [*1*:130f.; *67*:3, 10].

The fact that all the areas of the earth differ from each other leads also to a special interest in any cases in which separate areas appear to be alike. Closer examination reveals that they are never exactly alike, certainly not remotely as much alike as "two peas in a pod," nor even as two individuals of completely European ancestry may be alike in physical characteristics though born and raised on opposite sides of the Atlantic Ocean. Nevertheless, the ways in which separate areas are alike is no less significant than the ways in which they differ. Comparative study of such areas permits geography to approach the methods of laboratory sci-

16

ences, in which certain facts are controlled as constants, while others vary.

This purpose may appear to be excluded from a geography defined as "the study of areal differentiation" if one omits the phrase "the study of" and thus reads "differentiation" in the active sense—that is, "to differentiate." The purpose of close examination of areas which are somewhat alike is not to demonstrate that they differ, which we know must be the case without need of examination, but rather to determine how small or large the specific differences are. If such examination shows that in respect to certain individual features or groups of closely related features—for example, atmospheric conditions determining rainfall, temperature, cloudiness, etc., which we group together as climate—the differences among several areas are very slight, we say that such areas are "similar" in climate. We may then consider these areas, and all other areas of the world in which climatic conditions are "similar" in contrast to "dissimilar" conditions of other areas—that is, areas differing in minor degree in contrast to those differing in major degree—as specimen areas of the same type.

By this means we can construct a generic concept—for example, "Mediterranean type of climate"—which may be used to describe the climatic aspect of the character of any area (region) of that type. Or, in place of group concepts such as "Mediterranean" or "humid continental," in which all climatic conditions are considered together, we may establish generic concepts of the major constituents—rainfall, seasonal temperatures, etc.—and describe the total climate of any area of the world by combinations of these generic concepts, as in such symbolic forms as *BSh* (Koeppen) or *DA'W* (Thornthwaite).

Of course, in thus treating several areas as though quite alike in climate we have introduced a certain degree of error in our analysis of the character of areas. We may correct this, in larger scale analysis, by the use of more detailed generic concepts, expressed, for example, as *BShwg*. But no matter how far we continue this process there remain differences of some importance between any two parts of an area. This, of course, is the method by which we construct the well known systems of classification of areas of the world into various kinds of regions, sometimes called "generic regions," because they are based on generic concepts, whether of climate, landforms, soils, or agricultural systems [*1*:311–61].

"Similarity," therefore, is not the opposite of "difference," but merely a generalization under which differences deemed minor are ignored, those deemed major are emphasized. Some writers seek to avoid misunderstanding by speaking always of "differences and similarities," without recognizing that the phrase is redundant.[3] It may well be also that the repeated use of the term "differences" gives undue emphasis to the search for "contrasts." It therefore seems advisable to use the more neutral word, "variations."[4]

If the variations in diverse categories of phenomena which explorers and travelers reported from the many areas of the world —variations in such features as numbers, customs, occupations, and movements of people, in soils, landforms, and climate— showed no relation to each other beyond that of common location, geography would be little more than an organized catalogue or encyclopedia of facts about countries. Such an organized body of knowledge might satisfy the shallow curiosity of unsophisticated minds, and would be useful for business and statecraft, but it could not satisfy the desire for philosophical understanding. This intellectual interest has been present in mankind from the earliest recorded times. When travelers reported an unassorted and unrelated conglomeration of differences in diverse features in foreign areas, thoughtful scholars were concerned to organize these and explain them in terms of interrelations.

If these early writers depended more on imagination than on evidence, they were at least on the right track. There *are* signifi-

[3] Hettner on occasion used the double phrase, though noting its logical redundancy [*2*:275f.].

[4] The word which Hettner used most frequently, "*verschieden*," may be translated either as "different" or as "varying." A graduate student has called my attention to the fact that in the same paper in which Sauer introduced the term "areal differentiation" he also translated a statement of Hettner's as follows: "knowledge of the varying expression of the different parts of the earth surface" [*24*:22]. Hettner's original, in 1923, reads: "*die Wissenschaft von der verschiedenen Ausbildung der Erdoberfläche in ihren verschiedenen Teilen*" [*12*:37]. *Ausbildung* may also be translated as "development" or "formation."

cant interrelations among the variations in the diverse features of areas, and geographers at all times have been concerned to trace and demonstrate the connections that exist [*1*:120, 237–40].[5]

To emphasize the essential importance of such interrelationships in geography, Hettner, and other writers following him, included such phrases as "causally related," "causal connections," or "differences . . . interrelated with each other," in stating or expounding the concept of geography under discussion [*1*:92, 98, 142, 237f., 240–43, 335–37]. Nevertheless, numerous critics have inferred from the phrase "areal differentiation" that geography is *limited* "to the distinguishing of areas," or "to establishing differences from one area to another," or to "mere description."

A historical explanation for this misconception is suggested by certain comments in Spate's discussion. Whereas definitions of geography previously current in Britain and America always included the concept of relationships between man and nature, the definition in terms of "areal differentiation" is "austere" in that it "avoids reference to this time-honored concept" [*89*:15]. But surely in any science the study of its phenomena involves the study of relationships that may be found among them [*1*:120]. Students of astronomy, economics, geology, or zoology define their fields without mention of "relationships," or of "laws," evidently assuming that that goes without saying.[6] The unique feature of the traditional definition of geography in English-speaking countries, in concentrating on one particular class of relationships, those between man and nature, will be considered in Chapter VI.

The connections or causal relationships among the phenomena of geography, as Hettner noted in 1905, are of two kinds: the mutual relationships among different phenomena at one place,

[5] The title of Section III C of *The Nature of Geography* is misleading in labeling as one of the "Deviations from the Course of Historical Development," a concept of "Geography as a Science of Relationships" [*1*:120]. What is intended is clear in the first three paragraphs of the section. Geography, like any other science, strives "to understand the complex relationships existing among . . . the phenomena it studies." But geography is not to be defined merely as the study of those relationships, particularly not as "the study of relationships between nature and man." Obviously, the heading for this "Deviation" should read: "Geography Defined as the Science of the Relationships between Nature and Man."

[6] See, for example, the definitions of such fields in *The American College Dictionary,* in which scientific terms have been edited by professional consultants, listed by name in the introduction.

and relationships or connections between phenomena at different places [*11*:557; *1*:142, 240]. The latter necessarily involve movements across areas. Water and air, even pieces of solid materials, and, of course, animals, move from place to place producing interconnections of places.

With the introduction of man to the scene, this dynamic aspect in the character of areas becomes far more important; for it is one of the particular attributes of man that he not only moves from place to place himself, but sets other things in motion as well. It is especially in their human aspects, therefore, that areas differ not merely in their morphology, but also in what Ritter called their physiology, but which, to avoid the analogy with living organisms, we had better call their functional relations, involving movement among them.

Ullman has suggested that "areal differentiation" should be considered as a subconcept of geography as "spatial interaction" [*121*:60]. The suggestion seems to me to result from a misconception of the former term, if not also of the latter. Spatial interaction can only mean relations between phenomena in different places, and these phenomena, whether in place or in movement through space, form a part of the character of each area concerned. Hence the reverse is the case: variations in stationary characteristics, or forms, and variations in characteristics of movement, or functions, whether within an area or between it and another, are both included under the concept of areal variation, or differences in areas.

That both aspects are essential is not a new thought. It was clearly expressed by Ritter [*22*:48f.] and was included in Hettner's exposition of his concept of geography in 1905 [*11*:552; *2*:117; *1*:142]. Hettner indeed has warned against the exaggeration, for which he finds Ratzel in part responsible, of regarding space relations as the essential part of geography, to the neglect of differences in the content of areas [*2*:127f.; cf. Schmitthenner, *45a*:25].[7]

---

[7] This is not to imply that Ullman intends this exaggeration. His emphasis on "spatial interaction" [*121*;*122*] is a welcome reaction against a previous overemphasis on geographic thought in this country on morphology of areas, on forms and patterns at the expense of flows and functions. While this viewpoint is also criticized in numerous passages in *The Nature of Geography* [*1*:224–27, 281ff., 364], the lack of detailed consideration of the spatial interrelations of phenomena in that work undoubtedly reflects the general attitude of the period in which it was written [*1*:vii].

Several critics are concerned that Hettner's concept does not establish geography as a separate and distinct science, since other "field sciences" also study differences in areas. Hettner had explained that no such clear and sharp distinction should be expected, since all science is a unit which human limitations force us to divide more or less arbitrarily [2:110ff.; 1:142, 368]. The over-all point of view of geography, in its concern to analyze the character of places, differs in kind from that of a systematic science with its emphasis on analyzing a particular category of phenomena. The two points of view may be combined in particular studies, just as an economist may use the historical viewpoint and method. Whether such studies are to be considered as part of geography or as part of the systematic science, or both, is a minor question of classification, depending on the relative degree of emphasis of the respective viewpoints in the purpose of the particular study. The difference is well illustrated in Hugh Raup's discussion, in historic dependence on Humboldt,[8] of the distinction between "geographic botany" and "plant geography" [113: 346; similarly, Kalliola, 128]. The unique purpose of geography is to seek comprehension of the variable character of areas in terms of all the interrelated features which together form that variable character.

CONCLUSION

The objections that have been raised to the concept under discussion are directed for the most part against the particular term with which it has become identified and do not apply to the concept itself. Whether the objections to the term are warranted or not, the evidence seems convincing that by itself the term is inadequate. At the same time it says more than is necessary. For if we examine definitions of other sciences, we may conclude by analogy that it is superfluous to assert that geography studies

[8] In considering this aspect of what they call the "Humboldt-Ritter concept" of geography, Wooldridge and East unwittingly put Humboldt in argument with himself, in stating that he employed the concept outside of geography in his studies in "plant geography" [93:27]. Humboldt's statement of his concept of geography appears in his studies of "the geography of plants" as explanation of the differences between geography, including plant geography, and botany [1:77, 84, 135; 105:100].

"differences." Every science is a study of differences—otherwise little study would be needed.

We may therefore avoid numerous points of misunderstanding if we state simply that *geography is concerned to provide accurate, orderly, and rational description and interpretation of the variable character of the earth surface.* In its simplest form, as the "dean of French geographers," Cholley, states: "L'objet de la Géographie est la connaissance de la Terre" [52:14]; his subsequent discussion justifies, I believe, the additional words I have used.

The fact that this statement is not self-explanatory may be considered advantageous, for the moment at least. Each of the several terms used requires and will receive explanation. One phrase, "the variable character," has been described in full in this section. If the phrase "areal differentiation" can be accepted as a label referring to that full description, rather than whatever the two words may appear to mean from dictionary definitions, it may be convenient—though perhaps risky—to continue to use the term as a shorthand label, but only among professional colleagues who have learned what it is intended to represent.

can't understand these statements in
isdn - not self explan.

III.

What is Meant by the "Earth Surface"?

The formal limitation of the scope of geography to the outer shell of the planet is of relatively recent origin. As long as there was no generally recognized separation of astronomy and geography—as there was in ancient days and as late as the eighteenth century, when both were included under the term "cosmography"—no precise limitation was sought. Presumably the last scholar of high rank to consider them as parts of a single field was Alexander von Humboldt [*1*:83].

Even before Humboldt, Immanuel Kant appears to have considered geography and astronomy as distinct fields, although he did research in both. As a philosopher, his interest in geography was in that part of the earth that was the home of man, "so far as we can come into relation with it, the scene of our experiences" [*1*:40]. Other scholars of the late eighteenth century similarly pointed out that it was the concern of geography to study the earth as "the dwelling-place of man" [*1*:48], and early in the following century Ritter, among others, referred definitely to the "earth surface" as the scope of the field [*1*:41, 62; *22*:47].[1]

---

[1] Ritter restricted the scope of geography to the zone of the earth surface much more definitely than appears from the summary statement in *The Nature of Geography* [*1*:83]. It is true that he wrote at times of the planet or sphere, but in that case commonly added "as the home of man."

During much of the nineteenth century, however, many geographers argued—in no small part on semantic grounds—that geography (*Erdkunde*) included the entire planet, but in practice their work was necessarily confined almost entirely to the outer shell, depending on astronomers even for its over-all measurements. Since Richthofen's classic statement of 1883, few geographers have questioned that their field of work was limited to the outer shell of the earth—a limitation not likely to prove confining [*1*:115–20; cf. Hamelin, *57*:13].

Unfortunately we have found no fully satisfactory term for this portion of the planet with which we are concerned and, as Hettner noted in 1903, it is by no means easy to define precisely what we mean [*10*:23; *2*:231].

The term "earth surface" had long been current in German geography, and became established particularly through Richthofen's statements [*1*:41, 119]. A former geologist, Richthofen at first regarded *die Erdoberfläche* as the outer surface of the solid earth, treating this as the core subject of study in geography, and viewing other phenomena only as related to it. When he later broadened his concept of the object of direct study to a zone above and below the actual surface, he described that zone with the same term, "earth surface" [*21*:7f., 12f.].[2] The double meaning of the term is likewise reflected in the definition recently suggested by the Glossary Committee of British geographers: "While geography is immediately concerned with the surface of the Earth, it is customary to include the atmospheric envelope and the Earth's crust in the term Earth's surface in so far as they directly affect the surface." Not only does this statement provide a place for human geography merely by "custom," as Kinvig notes

[2] The uncertainty over the meaning of "earth surface" may well have contributed to the misconception that the object of study in geography was identical with "landscape" [*1*:149–58]. This English word can best be used in geography, as I have suggested, to mean "the external form of the earth surface under the atmosphere," comparable to the popular expression "the face of the earth" [*1*:162–65]. In approving this definition of "landscape," David Linton notes correctly that "it might have been framed with reference to air photographs" [*79*:27; cf. *1*:279], though not necessarily *vertical* air photographs, as he suggests, but photographs from all possible angles. The corresponding term in German geography is not *Landschaft*, since that term is also commonly used synonymously with "region," but rather *Landschaftsbild*.

[76:159]; it also implies that geography is more immediately concerned with landforms than with climates.

The concept of the "hydrosphere," which Mackinder suggested in 1931, but which few have adopted, comes closer to delimiting the physical scope of the field in which geographers actually work [18; 1:xxxii]. But the term is ambiguous, since it may or may not include the water vapor of the atmosphere; in any case we are neither exclusively nor primarily concerned with water. Rather, as Hettner stated in 1903, we are concerned with a shell of a certain thickness in which solid, liquid, and gaseous elements and the life forms dependent on them are found in interrelation with each other [10:23; repeated in 2:231].[3]

It seems unfortunate that the term Hettner used in stating this concept, *Erdhülle* ("earth envelope" or "earth shell"), was not accepted in preference to the traditional term *Erdoberfläche*. Richthofen had used the term *Erdhülle* in describing the thickness of the space above and below the mathematical surface of the earth which was to be included under the term "earth surface" [21:8, 16]. Likewise Ritter, in his celebrated lecture of 1833, had used a similar term in speaking of geography as the study of *"die erfüllten Räume der Planetrinde,"* and his further description emphasizes the fact that geography begins on the earth surface and extends deeper into the earth and higher above it with every new tool of observation [22:47f.].

The term "earth shell" has recently been brought back into use by Troll [47:163], and particularly by Hans Carol [32:113f.; 33]. As the object of geographic study, "the substance of geography" (*geographische Substanz*), Carol considers the earth shell as formed by the integration of elements of five different realms, the litho-, hydro-, atmo-, bio-, and anthroposphere, forming together the "geosphere." But it is necessary to emphasize that only the geosphere is a concrete reality; each of the other terms expresses an abstract classification.

It is still more difficult to find a suitable word for the concrete

[3] Hettner's concept corresponds in thought to Richthofen's statement of 1883 [1:119]. Vidal de la Blache used a very similar statement in 1913, and he also noted that the actual surface of the lithosphere has a particular interest because it preserves, in greater or less degree, the imprint of past modifications [27:293].

section of the earth shell which forms the object of a geographic study, covering less than the whole world. If the term "area" or "region" is used, it must be understood as having the thickness of the earth shell.[4]

A new question is raised by events occurring while this paper was in preparation. Man has for the first time projected his "world" of action beyond the atmosphere, that is, beyond what we could consider the earth shell, and may soon be expected to extend that range to the moon. Does this call for a change in the definition of geography? Presumably it would be permissible etymologically to expand the word "earth" to include all its satellites, both man-made and the moon itself, but we would be in logical difficulty when projectiles are sent to other planets.

The question will not be answered from etymology nor from logic alone, but from usage. Prior to experience, any answer offered now would be prediction, which is not the function of this study. But nothing that we now know suggests that the methods and tools of geography are likely to prove of first importance in securing knowledge of outer space.

CONCLUSION

In common speech we could most easily state the physical scope of the field of geography, as Kant and Lehmann have suggested, by speaking simply of the "world," without attempting more precise definition [*1*:119]. As a more technical term, the "earth shell" comes closest to the facts. But the term "earth surface" is deeply entrenched in our literature and is fairly satisfactory. No actual issues arise in substantive work; it is only in theoretical discussions that we have difficulty. If it seems a distortion of language to call a "shell" a "surface," we may remember that the distortion is quantitatively slight—the thickness of the earth shell we study is hardly one one-thousandth of its circumference.

[4] For such a section of the earth shell, Carol suggests the term *geomer*, formed by combining geosphere with the Greek word *meros* meaning "a part of a whole," and then shortening the combination. Further, he believes that the German word *Landschaft* may properly be defined as having the same meaning. If this is feasible in terms of common German usage, it is definitely not feasible to use the English word "landscape" to express this concept.

IV.

Is the Integration of Heterogeneous Phenomena

a Peculiarity of Geography?

ONE NEEDS ONLY to read through the program of papers of any of
the annual meetings of the Association of American Geographers
to observe the wide range of diverse phenomena which geographers study. "Topographic slope," Southern "neoplantations," in-
put-output analysis in modern industry, urban nodality, agriculture of the ninth century, place names and culture areas, and the
balance of power among the national states—all these and many
other topics appear to form direct subjects of study for geographers. Furthermore, a single study of a small area may include
within it no less a variety of topics.

In earlier periods in the development of knowledge, such heterogeneity was accepted as a matter of course. The earth and the
universe were recognized to be composed of a great variety of
things, and students were concerned to find out as much as possible about all things. Even in classical times, however, it was
learned—and relearned in the early development of modern science—that knowledge of the universe around us could progress
more rapidly and surely if its findings were organized in a systematic manner. Individual students and groups of students could
then specialize in particular kinds of problems and could make
use of the findings of previous students without the necessity of
being familiar with all the literature of all knowledge.

On this basis physics and chemistry developed as separate, though related, disciplines, each concentrating on a particular range of phenomena concerning material objects and substances. In other sciences students restrict their fields of study to particular categories: thus the botanist studies plants, the zoologist animals, the meteorologist the atmosphere, the geologist rocks. Likewise, in the fields concerned with the study of man in society—economics, political science, sociology, etc.—each field concentrates on particular aspects of social life.

In no case, to be sure, are these divisions absolute. The botanist studying the humid prairie of North America may need to consider the effect of Indian burnings, but he retains his focus of concern on the vegetation, and does not include Indian culture as an integral part of the field of botany.

The fields of science that are defined or delimited in the manner described above have commonly been called "the systematic sciences,"[1] although it should be noted that the division of the field of knowledge into kinds of materials studied is not necessarily the only feasible *system* of organization.

Geography is in marked contrast to these "systematic" fields, but it cannot be separated from them. The table of contents of almost any volume in "general geography" (or "systematic geography") published since Varenius established the subject demonstrates that geographers regard as integral parts of their field the same materials that form the objects of study in other fields [*1*: 130f., 434].

RECOGNITION OF THE PROBLEM

American geographers have long recognized this characteristic of their subject. To take but one of numerous examples available, Bowman, writing in 1934, had exclaimed: "How many physical subjects and new facts about them are involved! . . . Geography is the one subject that provides regional synthesis systematically" [*5*:39].

In England the question had been discussed by Mackinder, in 1887, in his earliest methodological statement, "On the Scope and

---

[1] Derived presumably from the term *systema naturae* which writers of the eighteenth century, or earlier, applied to the classification of phenomena by kind [*14*:65; *105*:101].

Methods of Geography." Observing that physical geography and geology "have data in part identical," he argued that "the data, though identical, are looked at from different points of view. They are grouped differently" [*16*:145]. Human geography (then called "political geography" in Britain) depended primarily on data used also in history. In consequence the two aspects of geography had come to be treated as separate fields, to the great detriment of human geography, which had lost its essential connection with the natural environment. Successful development of geography, Mackinder urged, requires that it be treated as a unified single discipline in spite of the great variety of phenomena included within it.

Mackinder's programmatic address of 1887 echoed viewpoints current at the time in German geography.[2] These were based on the classic works of Humboldt and more specifically on the methodological essays of Carl Ritter, which were critically reconsidered by such students as Peschel, Marthe, and Ratzel [*1*:53, 80].

In Ritter's discussions heterogeneity of phenomena was not only accepted but stressed as an essential characteristic of geography. The subject finds its unity and distinction as a field of knowledge in the study of the character of areas as determined by the multiplicity of features which, in interrelation with each other, fill the areas of the earth surface [*1*:56f.]. Humboldt described even more explicitly the contrast between the similarity of phenomena studied in each of the systematic sciences with the great heterogeneity of phenomena which must be studied in geography. While this makes far more difficult the construction and application of laws of relationships, it is essential for the special purpose of geography, "the comprehension of unity in multiplicity" (*Erkenntniss der Einheit in der Vielheit*) [*14*:55, 65]. If this viewpoint, which Humboldt expressed in many of his sentences, was not recognized by students who were familiar primarily with his topical studies, such as those in the geography of plants, it was clearly explained and demonstrated in

---

[2] While Mackinder's address of 1887 gives no direct indication of familiarity with the work in German geography, we know that by 1895 he was able to write with knowledge of the work in that country in his paper on "Modern Geography, German and English" [*17*].

his regional studies in Spanish American areas [*1*:65, 68, 76f.].[3]

Following the deaths of Humboldt and Ritter, however, geography had no place in German universities until its rapid expansion in the decades following the unification of Germany in 1871. This expansion brought into the field men who had been trained not in geography but in a great variety of other fields [*1*:106; *41*:411]. Widely divergent viewpoints led to vigorous methodological discussion and the increasing divergence of physical and human geography.[4]

This divergence of viewpoint was climaxed by Gerland's proposal that in order to qualify as a distinct field in a systematic division of the sciences geography should confine itself to the natural features of the earth planet [*1*:89f., 106–15]. Misconstruing Ritter's famous phrase, *die irdisch erfüllten Räume der Erdoberfläche,* he argued that "a science of the heterogeneous things that fill area is impossible because of their heterogeneity" [*1*:57, 114]. Critics at the time pointed out that even under Gerland's limitation the field would include a diversity of phenomena comparable to that of all the natural sciences, other than astronomy. If heterogeneity must be eliminated, his proposal was but one step in a series of which the logical consequence would be the disintegration of the field of geography.

Even before Gerland made his proposal, the methodological discussion of the period had reached what was to prove to be its positive culmination in the inaugural address which Richthofen made at Leipzig in 1883, expressing a viewpoint which came to be accepted in subsequent decades by the great majority of German students [*1*:91f.]. Drawing on the statements of both Humboldt and Ritter, Richthofen recognized that geography cannot seek its distinctive place in science in terms of any particular category of phenomena but rather in terms of its viewpoint and method. The

---

[3] The presentation of Humboldt's methodological views in *The Nature of Geography* has since been confirmed and greatly amplified by Stevens-Middleton in his chapter on "Aspectos Epistemologicos de la Obra de Humboldt" [*129*:199–246].

[4] The course of these debates can most readily be followed in the series of critical surveys which Hermann Wagner contributed, under the title "Bericht über die Methodik der Erdkunde" in the *Geographisches Jahrbuch*, Vols. VII, VIII, IX, X, XII, and XIV (1878–90).

distinctive purpose of geography is to study the formation in the earth surface of the multiplicity of phenomena into unity *(Vielheit zur Einheit)*. The chorological viewpoint analyzes how the most heterogeneous materials of areas are joined together by causal relationships to form the character of the different areas of the world, and of the world as a whole [*21*:25–28, 65–67].

Examining the field of geography nearly half a century later, from the point of view of a philosopher of science, Kraft observed: "Stones, plants, animals and man, in themselves objects of their own sciences, constitute objects in geography insofar as they are of importance for, or characteristic of, the nature of the earth surface" [*1*:143].

Similar statements may be found in the writings of French geographers from the earliest methodological statement of Vidal de la Blache [*26*] to the present. Thus Cholley contrasts the aim of geography with that of the systematic sciences of nature and man: "It is a form of abstraction to isolate the individual facts in categories—facts of climate, of relief, of vegetation, of human activity—but the reality which geography studies is the fact of their multiple combinations, that is to say, of the diverse habitats *(milieux)* which they form" [*52*:14–15, 21–25].

The conclusion reached by German geographers toward the end of the last century, that geography is concerned to study the character and interrelations of areas as determined by a great diversity of associated phenomena, was not developed by deduction from any special theory of the relation of geography to other sciences. Rather it developed out of their experience, by induction from the intrinsic characteristics of the geographic work of their predecessors as well as their own [*1*:98].

In general, most geographers today, as throughout the past history of the field, accept fields of corn, soil, forests, landforms, railroads, cities, and states as proper objects of study in their field. But nevertheless most geographers find it difficult to explain to students in other fields what it is that geography studies.

ATTEMPTS TO ESCAPE THE PROBLEM

The effort to provide an answer to the question of what distinctive phenomena form the objects of study in geography led a generation ago to the attempt to discover or invent objects which geography alone could claim to study. "Landscapes" (in German, *Landschaften*) were considered as material objects, and at the same time, thanks to the double meaning of the German word, could be considered as limited areas, like regions [*1*:149–58]. Hence the concept of the "region" as a unitary, concrete object existing in reality [*1*: Chapter IX]. These attempts have passed into history, but the persistence of the desire to find such a justification for the recognition of geography as a systematic science is demonstrated by recurrent attempts to revive the concept of the region as reality—even though that concept was shown to be illusory more than a century ago by Bucher [*1*:46, 268].

If such attempts represented a striving for the advantages of specialization, by restriction to a narrower range of phenomena, they would merit serious consideration. But even if we could establish the theoretical proposition that the landscape is a region and the region therefore an object, to say that the distinctive objects of study in geography are regions, would not alter the fact that to study regions we must study directly a great heterogeneity of things. Even if we accepted a limitation of geography to things physically observable, we would still be directly concerned with an enormous variety of different kinds of objects; further, since all physical features created by man are consequences of non-material factors—customs, institutions, etc.—the theoretical limitation would not in fact reduce the variety of factors the geographer must analyze [*1*:218].

It is not by narrowing the scope of their field that geographers can achieve specialization, as Mackinder noted in 1887: "For this purpose either physical or political (human) geography would be as unwieldy as the entire subject." Specialization must be developed by individual students and groups of students within geography itself, but "as a basis for all fruitful specialization within the subject, we insist on the teaching and grasping of geography as a whole" [*16*:145].

Likewise we could not escape from the essential heterogeneity of geography by asserting that the subject is limited to the study of the spatial arrangement of phenomena in an area, in contrast to the phenomena themselves [*116*:228, 243f.; *104*:214, 237]. For interpretation of the relations of phenomena requires understanding of the character of the diverse phenomena whose interrelations extend over space.

"THE INTEGRATION OF HETEROGENEOUS PHENOMENA"

The synthesis of the interrelations of phenomena that give character to area is a form of integration—though by no means the only example of the use of integration in scientific work.

A study in a systematic field involves not only analysis but also synthesis of a number (it may be a multiplicity) of factors. Further, the factors which need to be considered in, say, a systematic study in botany, may be of quite heterogeneous character, including those of climate, soil materials, animal life, and human activity. But the study starts with the selection of a particular kind of object, plants, which are mentally extracted from the complex of phenomena surrounding them, may even be removed to the laboratory for analysis, and form the ultimate focus of the study. In geography, in contrast, the interest is focused from the start on the existing integrations of diverse phenomena which, by their existence, determine the variable character of area [*1*:67f.; 145f., 283f., 373; cf. Watson, *3*:465f.; Hamelin, *57*:8f.]. It begins, that is, with things as they are actually arranged and interrelated in reality, even as the layman may observe them [cf. Vidal de la Blache, *27*:299].

While the geographer starts at the same level as the observant layman, and each necessarily selects or emphasizes particular features out of all that is observable in an area, in order to analyze the variable character of area the geographer must use some systematic and purposeful methods of selection. In concentrating on one category of features at a time, he will observe the varying manifestations of that particular category, in relation to those of other categories with which the variations are most closely interrelated. By this method he may establish the existence of systems and areal patterns of particular categories which the layman is unable to observe, and by comparison of such areal patterns of different categories induce hypotheses of process relationships among the different phenomena.

In comparing the character of our field, as presented in *The Nature of Geography*, with that of cultural anthropology, Robert Anderson raises a question which is similar to the challenge which Gerland asserted many decades ago. Following views ascribed to Leslie White and Kroeber, he concludes that progress in knowledge requires autonomy in investigation in each of the three distinct levels of reality—inorganic, organic, and superorganic or cultural. Since geography groups phenomena on disparate levels, "discovery of intercausal relations must be extremely difficult" [97:133–35].

We must presume that Anderson does not mean that a botanist studies plants without considering differences in climate or soil, or that cultural anthropology takes no account of differences in the inorganic and organic bases of cultures. Undoubtedly there are advantages for the student of a systematic science who can concentrate his thinking about relationships either in terms of inorganic processes, or organic processes, or cultural processes. Certainly the discovery of intercausal relations is more difficult when variations in two or all three levels are involved, as they are in geography.

The fact is, however, that such complexes do exist in integrations which vary areally and form the reality of the world in which we live. Division of the study of that reality into separate sciences may provide explanations of the various parts of these integrations, but it offers no approach to synthetic description or explanation of the total integration of areas. The total reality is there for study, and geography is the name of the section of empirical knowledge which has always been called upon to study that reality. Whether such a study can be a "science" is a semantic question which we will postpone to a later chapter (Chapter X).

We will also need to consider later (Chapter IX) the methods by which geography seeks both to break down the infinite complexity of the total character of area into manageable segments, and to comprehend the integrated complex of all such interrelated phenomena in different areas. It is necessary, however, to note here that in dividing the total integration of phenomena in areal variation we do not find that the inorganic, organic, and cultural phenomena form segments, each of which constitutes a more closely integrated part of the total. The fact that human life depends in general on plant and animal life, that animal life depends in general on plant life, and plant life on the inorganic world does not mean that individual relationships among phenomena at different levels follow the same order.

Thus, in studying the areal variation of plant life, we cannot think in terms of its relation to a separately existing integration of rainfall, temperature, inorganic soil material, slope, and drainage; these elements are related to each other in a variety of separate ways, or they may be quite unrelated. The establishment of a close integration is the work of the vegetation itself. Cultural phenomena likewise may be directly related to particular inorganic phenomena, as in the case of mining industries in relation to ore deposits, with little or no participation of other inorganic or organic elements.

Geography therefore studies phenomena of unlimited variety in interrelationships of the greatest variety. This is not to be considered as a by-product of the nature of geography, or as a characteristic which, though common to all fields, is somewhat more marked in geography than in others. Rather it is fundamental to the very purpose of geography as the study of the reality of the earth surface, composed as that is of all kinds of things in all kinds of combinations. Studies of individual categories of phenomena are appropriately assigned to the several systematic sciences. The distinctive purpose of geography is to study the variations over the earth of phenomena which exist in interrelation, regardless of the classification of the phenomena by kind.

COMPARISON WITH OTHER FIELDS

To contrast geography, concerned with an almost unlimited heterogeneity of phenomena, with the sciences that select particular categories of phenomena for study is not to say that geography is unique or exceptional among the sciences. Nearly all geographers who have accepted the view of geography here presented recognize that much the same is true of the field of history [1:183, 283]. Humboldt specifically noted that not only human history but the history of all life and the history of the earth resemble geography in this respect more than they do the other sciences.

Astronomy was considered by Humboldt as logically similar to geography, the two forming a single science concerned with the unity of diversity in the universe. But the great difference in degree of heterogeneity of observable phenomena greatly simplifies the study of the celestial areas as compared with the terrestrial areas [*14*:56–59]. Other students who have noted that astronomy includes a heterogeneity of phenomena, limited only by what actually exists or can be observed in the heavens, include Vallaux in France and William Morris Davis in this country [*1*:142, 371].

CONCLUSION

In every branch of science the phenomena of direct concern vary to some degree in character, and every branch of science studies the ways in which these phenomena are interrelated, or integrated, with other phenomena. In what we have called the systematic sciences, however, the extent of heterogeneity is limited and the degree of integration is but partial, because each of these sciences defines its field of study in terms of a selected category of phenomena. In those fields which are defined not in terms of kinds of phenomena but in terms of sections of time or space, the integrations which are to be analyzed are infinitely complex, and the heterogeneity of phenomena to be studied is limited only by the phenomena which exist and vary within the given sections of time and space.

In the space sciences, other than geography, the phenomena as yet observable are limited to inanimate nature. In history, as limited to the short period of literate history, natural phenomena have been relatively constant, so that in the integrations which history studies, the variable factors are largely limited to human elements. The earth surface is unique to our knowledge as an object which consists of integrations formed by a great diversity of inanimate, biological, and social phenomena, varying in significant interrelations from place to place. The goal of geography, the comprehension of the earth surface, involves therefore the analysis and synthesis of integrations composed of interrelated phenomena of the greatest degree of heterogeneity of perhaps any field of science.

V.

———————

What Is the Measure of "Significance" in Geography?

———————

IT IS ONE THING to speak of the total complex of heterogeneous phenomena whose integration in terms of place the geographer is concerned to analyze. It is quite another matter (as Stephen Jones has pointed out in correspondence with me concerning certain passages in *The Nature of Geography* and in an early draft of this paper) to carry out such an analysis [cf. De Jong, *34*]. Indeed, on the basis of what has been said in the previous chapter, we must recognize that complete analysis of the "total complex" is not only impractical but is not to be postulated as the theoretical goal. For such a goal would require, even in the study of a single small area, analysis of a literally endless list of incommensurable elements, and the resultant publication could not be contained on a five-foot bookshelf.

We are therefore forced, even in theory, to find some rational and consistent basis for considering in our studies something less than the complete number of variable features involved in the total complex of any place. What common measuring rod can we use to determine which features should be selected as more rather than less significant in forming the variable character of area?

VARIOUS SOLUTIONS THAT HAVE BEEN OFFERED

Twenty years ago a large number of geographers sought to answer this question by restricting the phenomena of study in geography to physical things, or even to visually perceptible objects. Thorough examination of this idea demonstrated that such limitation was contrary to the development of our field and created more problems than it solved [*1*: Chapter VII].[1]

Cholley, in discussing fundamental principles in geography, urges that since the ultimate objective is knowledge of the whole world a sense of proportion requires consideration only of those materials which could enter into a rational construction of the world, leaving aside purely accidental or local phenomena [*52*:14, 19–21]. Certainly phenomena which are found repeatedly over the world are more significant to an understanding of its total character than are those occurring uniquely. But, as Cholley recognizes, I believe, in other connections, a geography limited to consideration of generic cases would not describe and interpret the particular combinations of phenomena of individual places, each of which is unique.

Further, limitation to the generic is not in itself sufficient to protect geography from the danger Ritter noted long ago of taking over from other sciences the listing of generic items "even to the smallest kinds of insects and mosses," so that geography "takes on the colors of the other sciences without developing its own distinctive character" [*23*:28].

The distinctive character of geography, as most of the students we have quoted agree, is its concern with the integrated combinations of phenomena as interrelated spatially, interrelated among themselves at any one place and interrelated across space with those of other areas. On this basis, Hettner concluded, in a statement first published in 1905, that the phenomena for study in geography include only those which account for the variable character of the earth surface, because their variations are interrelated with those of other phenomena, whether at the same place or in different places [*2*:129f.; *1*:240ff.].

[1] According to Uhlig, this issue in German geography, though unresolved, has lost its significance in practice. Not geography as a whole, but only *Landschaftskunde*, as one major part of it, is restricted to the study of visible phenomena, and the interpretation of the physiognomy of the landscape brings back into consideration whatever nonvisible or nonmaterial elements are needed for the interpretation [*48*:1–5, 17–22]. Whatever value there may be in first excluding nonmaterial phenomena from original observation only to bring them back later, the concept offers no effective method of restricting the phenomena which geographers are to study [*1*:213–15].

Considered as a practical rule in the difficult problem of determining which of the myriad number of phenomena that vary areally should be selected for inclusion in a geographic study, the statement seems little more than common sense. No doubt most geographers follow some such rule in practice. Geography cannot present all the facts about areas any more than history could record everything that has ever happened. In either field, as a study of phenomena in integration, nothing is lost by omitting phenomena, however prominent, which have little or no connection with other phenomena. Conversely, as Gradmann stated in 1919, "the individual fact enters (into a geographic study) with a degree of importance that increases with the extent to which it is interlaced, on many sides and internally, with neighboring circles of phenomena, both forward and backward as cause and effect" [*1*:242].

The form of Gradmann's statement reminds us that our concern is not to set up rules for excluding this or that topic or phenomenon. Indeed we cannot be certain that Hettner's criteria, if considered negatively, would necessarily exclude any phenomenon of the earth surface—who can say that it is in *no* way related to other areal phenomena? But since the variety and quantity of phenomena that might be considered are so vast and vary so greatly in degree of importance in the total picture, serious students of knowledge must seek a positive criterion for selecting what is of greater rather than of lesser significance.

In practice we do this by a series of trial-and-error processes. Since we cannot begin with a study of the totality of areal variation, we must begin with a particular aspect or topic which, on the basis of general knowledge of many areas or reconnaissance observation of a particular area, we believe to be so interrelated with other areal phenomena as to constitute a significant aspect for study. Investigation may demonstrate that this is not the case, that in fact the topic selected shows little relation in its areal variation to those of other phenomena and hence is of but minute importance to the totality of areal variation. Such a study therefore contributes primarily to knowledge about that phenomenon in itself, that is, it is of concern to the systematic science in which the phenomenon is classified.

If the variation over an area of the phenomenon initially selected for investigation is found to be of major importance in the total variation of the area, interpretative study of that variation will necessarily lead to variations of other phenomena that appear to be related to it. Whatever can be shown to be thus interrelated is to be included, to the degree that its interrelation indicates. Since interrelationships may be significant but not obvious, it is often necessary to attempt to conjecture probable or possible relationships that need to be tested before deciding whether or not they should be included.

If the study is intended to cover the complete geography of an area, the investigation of all the apparent relationships or connections with the phenomena first selected may appear to involve considerably less than the total areal variation. One may then start again with a new category of phenomena which appear to be independently but significantly related to other kinds of areal variation. Pursuing this new route of investigation, it is highly likely that the student will uncover relationships with the areal variations included in the first set, relationships which were not perceived in that part of the study. If all relationships could be perceived, it seems probable that a single continuous progression from one important category of areal variation through another related to it and so to the next would ultimately produce analysis of all the significantly related areal variations. To the degree that lack of data or inability to perceive relationships produces discontinuities, it is necessary to make several fresh starts.

The emphasis on the relevance of interrelations and interconnections in determining the relative importance to geography of the diverse phenomena varying in area has been criticized by some readers as a dangerous backsliding to the principle of "environmentalism," to the concept of geography as "the study of relationships" between man and nature.[2] This reaction appears to

---

[2] Schlüter raised this objection to Hettner's criteria for selection of phenomena more than fifty years ago, when they were both engaged in combatting the "environmentalist" concept of geography [cf. *1*:120–26, especially note 47]. Schlüter himself was advocating the limitation of geography to sensually perceptible phenomena [*1*:190 *et al*]. In reviving this issue in his recent study of Schlüter's contribution to methodology, Lautensach presents what seems to me an effective brief of but one side of the argument [*36*:219f.].

result from certain misunderstandings concerning the meaning and place of "relationships" in geography.

First, when we say that geography studies the complex features formed by phenomena in interrelation, this is not the same as to say that relationships constitute the subject of study [1:243].[3] If there were no interrelations among the phenomena, other than juxtaposition, geography would be no more than an encyclopedic compendium of little intellectual value.

The second misconception results from the habit engendered by environmentalism of identifying the word "relationships" in geography as meaning relationships between nature and man. Hence the criterion sounds similar to environmentalist statements of geography which appear to accept natural features on their own account, and human features only as related to those of nature. It is necessary to rid ourselves of the idea that geography is peculiarly concerned with relationships across the abstract line between human and natural. In our concern to analyze the integrated features which produce the variable character of areas, any interlocking of different elements may be of concern—for example, the synthesis of plant life, climate, and soil in producing variations in vegetative cover.

In considering what natural features to include in their studies, geographers have in fact commonly ignored those which contribute little (either in themselves or in integration with other elements) to the total integration of areas. Only rarely do we find relevant the terrestrial variations of such phenomena as magnetic declination, the distribution of fossils, or countless details of stratigraphy, which geologists find of great importance for their studies.

The problem of selection is of greatest importance in respect to human phenomena because of the unlimited number of areal variations that can be observed. To use examples suggested by Plewe, should a study of the geography of western Europe include consideration of such items as the differences in contents of national art galleries, or of types of construction of railway bridges over the Rhine, or of cathedral architecture [41:412]? It is not necessary to give an a priori answer to this question. It is sufficient

[3] See footnote 5 in Chapter II.

to say that whatever is found to be significantly relevant to other areal variations should be considered to the degree found to be relevant. In many cases the student may legitimately save time by judging that such relationship is most improbable; in a much larger number of cases the degree of relevance can only be determined by investigation.[4]

Regardless of theoretical arguments, as it was suggested earlier, most geographers who stop to ask themselves which phenomena to emphasize and which to overlook appear to make their decisions more or less along the line indicated by Hettner's criterion. But if we agree in principle that we are most concerned with those features which contribute most, indirectly as well as directly, to the character of an area, what is the measure of the somewhat vague concept of "character" (*Wesen*)? In contrast, the concept of the appearance of the area (landscape, or *Landschaftsbild*) is a concrete measurable quality, but as Schlüter was forced to recognize, mere appearance does not provide a satisfactory measure of importance [*1*:192]. Apparently most German geographers have in practice found neither concept satisfactory, as Plewe suggests, and fall back on "geographic judgment" [*41*:413].

JUDGMENT IN PRACTICE

In the search for a sound theoretical statement, it may be helpful to consider what geographers have done in practice, regardless of theory. Looking at geography from the point of view of the philosophy of science, Kraft concluded that man and his works occupy a more prominent place in geography than would be expected from standard definitions of the subject [*15*:5f.]. An attempt was made to answer his challenge in *The Nature of Geography* by emphasizing the major role that man plays in producing differences from place to place in the earth surface [*1*:144]. Hettner, in effect, had said much the same thing in explaining the importance of man in geography as a special case of his general rule that what is

---

[4] Schlüter objected, and Lautensach currently repeats the objection, that Hettner's thesis produces a closed circle: a student is not to study phenomena unless they are interrelated, but he cannot know that they are interrelated unless he studies them [*36*:225]. But as Hettner had indicated, this problem is common to all scientific study; it is necessary to investigate possible relationships that may prove to be blind alleys [*1*:241].

decisive in the selection of material is "the significance to other categories of phenomena" [2:131]. Similarly Deffontaines speaks of man, *homo faber,* as the agency having greatest effect on the character of the earth surface [54:5].

These answers still fail, it seems to me, to explain fully why we select as we do in geography. They still provide no measure for "significance," particularly in the study of earth features over which man has had but little influence.

If we consider climatology, isn't it clear that what geographers seek in this field is analysis and measurement of climatic elements as significant, ultimately, to man? Herbertson recognized that in making his classic map of "natural regions" (in fact primarily climatic regions) what he really meant was "regions based on natural conditions as significant to man" [1:300].

In geomorphology a major criterion no doubt has been that of appearance. More of the world is covered by hills than by mountains, but mountains have a greater interest because they dominate the landscape.[5] But "appearance" is a meaningful word only in terms of the beholder. Hence the appearance of an area, as one of the aspects of its character, is part of its significance to man. If one considers the more specific details of geomorphological description, such as the determination of elevations and slopes, the significant differences noted are also those significant for man.

The thesis is most clearly illustrated in the division of Germany into "natural areas" (*die naturräumliche Gliederung Deutschlands*), the collective work of a large number of German geographers [43]. While limited to "strictly natural elements," examination of the criteria used for distinguishing areas demonstrates, as Schmithüsen has stated, that these have been considered and evaluated in terms of significance for the natural vegetation and for human use [cf. Carol, 32:120].

The fact is that throughout history geographers have looked upon the earth not simply as a physical (natural) body but as that physical body which is the home of man [1:48; similarly Spate, 87:419f.]. Varenius, the author of the first great work on

---

[5] Hettner, it may be noted, on occasion included in his criteria for selection of material, in addition to those noted earlier, "phenomena which are significant to the appearance" of an area [2:231; from 10:23].

systematic geography, justified the view of the Earth as at least equally important with the rest of the Universe, on the grounds that "not only is the Earth our home—the abode of the human race—but from her we take our origins and she gives us the means of our preservation and of the propagation of our kind" [according to J. N. L. Baker, *62*:60].

For Ritter and his followers, the purpose of studying the physical aspects of the earth was to demonstrate the divine plan by which the earth formed the dwelling and nurturing place of man. Even those who turned away from this teleological concept to concentrate on physical geography for its own sake have tended to justify the inclusion of their studies as part of geography because an understanding of the physical earth was essential to the geography of man. For Wooldridge and East "the physical aspects are literally basic to a full geography" [*93*:40], and similar expressions may be found in numerous studies of French geographers.

Indeed it is difficult to imagine how we could study the non-human features of the earth without thought of their significance to man. The term commonly used in our literature to refer to these features, "natural environment," indicates that which environs man. As Sauer puts it, "environment is a term of cultural appraisal" [*115*:8]; what we call "natural environment" can only be described in terms of the knowledge and preferences of the occupying persons; " 'natural resources' are in fact cultural appraisals" [quoted by Kinvig, *76*:160]. To illustrate "the fallacy of thinking of environment apart from the environed, instead of 'environment for what,' " Spate fancifully suggests a study of "Principles of Piscine Geography" [*87*:419], as *The Nature of Geography* suggested mapping "natural regions" in reference to mosquitoes or to sequoias [*1*:300].

To think of nature as "natural environment," however, is a particular orientation implying a special hypothesis, the "environmentalist" concept of man as influenced or determined by the natural conditions in which he lives. Writing in 1905, when this concept still had some adherents in Germany, Hettner attacked the view that physical geography studied the earth surface *nur als Wohn- und Erziehungshaus des Menschen* ("only as the dwelling- and nurturing-home of man") ; this was a teleological distortion, stemming from Ritter. "The nature of the lands is in the first place there for itself and must be studied and understood for itself" [*11*:560; repeated in *2*:125]. But, as noted earlier, we find no clear answer to the question of just what, in the total nature of the lands, we are to select for study.

BASIC THEORY

To find the answer to our problem we may ask ourselves the most elementary question, namely, why should there be such a field as geography itself—why, that is, put so much effort in studying such a minute part of the total universe, dividing that minute part into many still more minute divisions, in each of which we find after all only varying combinations of much the same elements? The answer, surely, is that this minute part of the universe, including the rays of light and heat that enter it from heavenly bodies or from the interior of the earth, is in fact our universe, the world in which we live and which we can directly experience. What to the astronomer is only the outer shell of one of the minor planets of one of the lesser stars in one of innumerable galaxies is to all mankind our world and the only world we know.

Geography is not therefore merely like all of science in being anthropocentric because only man studies science. The subject of study in geography, the world—even in those parts of it in which there are no men—is viewed as man's world.

Cholley has expressed this most definitely as the final conclusion of his examination of the nature of geography, in a statement which has been so often echoed in the writings of other French geographers that we repeat it here in the original: *La conception géographique s'avère en définitive comme une sorte de philosophie de l'homme considéré comme l'habitant principal de la planète* ("the geographical conception is in the last analysis a kind of philosophy of man considered as the principal inhabitant of the planet") [*52*:121]. The expression, however, is easily misunderstood; specifically its meaning for me is greatly changed by the form in which Le Lannou puts it: "geography is the knowledge of man considered as an inhabitant of the planet" [*58*:273]. I should wish to restate it: geography is man's study of the earth as the planet of which he is the principal inhabitant.

To test Cholley's thesis, let us suppose that the human race should use its recently discovered powers to destroy itself, and were ultimately succeeded by a race of literate insects who learned to read our books through minimizers. They could accept our physics and chemistry, and the greater part of other natural sciences with little change, but might find it necessary to completely rewrite the physical (not to mention the "human") branches of geography. In the study of landforms, soils, climates, and plants, they would conclude, we had passed over the critical distinctions, selecting in their place distinctions of little value for the new heirs of the earth [*1*:299f.].

In short, whatever features of the earth surface the geographer analyzes, he inevitably thinks of them in terms of significance to man. Schmitthenner, in partial dependence on Plewe, states the principle perhaps in clearest form: *In der Geographie . . . ist der Mensch das Mass* ("In geography, man is the measure") [*44*:128].

To accept man's interest as the measuring rod of significance in all parts of geography does not, to be sure, provide a single unitary criterion. "Our terrestrial home," as Wooldridge rightly insists, is not merely the theater of economic processes, it is also— and for every child should be first—"a thing of beauty and of interest"; it is of concern to man to understand "how our terrestrial home is constructed, the meaning of its scenery and of the patterns of its sky" [*92*:45–47].[6]

It is likewise true that the features of the earth have a different significance for peoples of different cultures, or of different times, and for different groups and individuals within the same time and culture. There is therefore ample room for a great variety of different and incommensurable interests in geography conceived in terms of the interest of man. Even the scholar who selects according to his own eccentric interests may be recognized as contributing to that degree of human interest in geography, but he must accept the fact that others are under no obligation to share his interests.

[6] To quote Wooldridge at this point is not to assert that he is in agreement with the thesis of this chapter, but if I understand these and similar expressions rightly, and can induce correctly his view of the function of geomorphology in geography, he is concerned with landforms and other natural features in proportion to their significance for man.

The problem of selecting in terms of significance to man has always been present in the study of geography. If the polar expeditions of Amundsen and Scott had been able to provide a thorough geographical survey of the Antarctic continent, in terms of contemporaneous evaluation of what was significant, we might today require a complete resurvey, not because of any errors on their part or because of any change in Antarctica, but because it did not occur to them to determine whether there were uranium deposits in any part of that vast area [cf. *1*:300].

CONCLUSION

If we recognize that "significance" in geography is measured, consciously or unconsciously, in terms of significance to man, we may readily add that measure to the criteria which Hettner offered for the selection of earth features for inclusion in the study of areas [*1*:240, 242]. Conspicuous or strange objects or forms in the landscape may arouse curiosity out of proportion to their significance to whatever aspect of geography one is studying, or to the total variation of area as significant to man. Any phenomenon, whether of nature or of man, is significant in geography to the extent and degree to which its interrelations with other phenomena in the same place or its interconnections with phenomena in other places determines the areal variations of those phenomena, and hence the totality of areal variation, measured in respect to significance to man. Such interrelations need not be between human and natural features; climatic differences that produce differences in natural vegetation are more significant to man than those that do not.

The conclusion that geography selects from the unlimited variety of earth features those significant to man likewise explains the historical fact that the scope of the field has been limited to the thin outer shell of the earth which forms man's world. In this sense, we may accept the expression used by countless students since the eighteenth century that geography studies "the earth as the home of man" [*1*:48, 60, 61, 63].

The word "home," however, is not to be considered literally as "domicile," nor in the sense which Allix expresses as merely the area of human occupation [*49*:296], nor in our traditional sense of "environment," but rather in the fullest sense as that part of the physical universe which constitutes the world we experience. It includes not merely the solid and liquid shell of the earth and the lower atmosphere in which we move, but the visible skies above, varying from place to place on the earth in cloudiness and clarity, in color by day and in constellations by night.

It is also necessary to pin down the elusive preposition "as." We study the earth not as something related to man and hence only in the ways in which it is related to man, but as an object in itself. But the scope of that object and the selection of phenomena included in it are determined by our basic interest in the object as we experience it.

With these specific qualifications, we may further modify our original statement: geography is that discipline that seeks *to describe and interpret the variable character from place to place of the earth as the world of man.*

VI.

Must We Distinguish Between Human and Natural Factors?

A PASSAGE IN *The Nature of Geography* concerning the semantic problems of the words "natural" and "nature" concludes that such terms are needed to express the contrast between the part of reality which is independent of man and that part which is "human," because "the relations between the world of man and the nonhuman world are of greatest concern in geography" [*1*: 298f.].

This statement is asserted without qualification or explanation, even though it is recognized in the same passage that "for Humboldt, as well as his predecessors," the word "natural" was used to include all the phenomena observed outside the observer's mind—objective reality. In fact, neither Humboldt nor Ritter seemed to feel any need for a term to designate the particular category of relations which the geographer of the year 1939 described as "of greatest concern in geography."[1]

---

[1] While Humboldt, as far as I can find, was consistent in his use of the term "nature," Ritter's writings reveal an inconsistency in this respect, as in many others. Thus we find him speaking of *die Menschenwelt und die Naturwelt* (according to Tatham, in his penetrating and thoroughly documented discussion of (German) "Geography in the Nineteenth Century" [*3*:43]) . Indeed, it may well be that Ritter's teleological concept of the earth as divinely planned in full detail for the development of the human race might be considered as one of the historic roots of the particular emphasis in geography on the relations between man and (nonhuman) nature. More generally, the concept seems consistent with the viewpoint of the Book of Genesis.

We may note also that those unknown but undoubtedly very numerous persons of reflective mind, who from earliest times recognized that the differences in the diverse earth phenomena from place to place were in some way related to each other, do not appear to have felt a need for emphasis on this distinction. It is not mere chance that until very recent times there was no common word to describe the whole of nature minus man.

Are we perhaps to conclude that geographers studying the earth during the past century have developed the ability, which their predecessors lacked, to separate the world of man and the nonhuman world as objective entities? In other passages of *The Nature of Geography* it is argued that this is not the case. The contrast between the "natural landscape" and the "cultural landscape," which at the time of writing played such an important part in the thinking of many geographers, is shown to be a purely theoretical concept. There can be only one landscape in any place: if man has not been there, it cannot be a cultural landscape; if man has entered the scene, the natural landscape is forever lost [*1*:170–74, 300–303].

Granted that the distinction is only theoretical or abstract, it might be that in the development of intellectual tools for research geographers had demonstrated that this abstract distinction aided their search for knowledge. This is certainly denied by several arguments. Thus it is asserted that many students confuse as one concept what is actually three: the "primeval landscape," that is, the original natural landscape before the entry of man; the "wild landscape," one that has been altered but not controlled by man; and the present "natural landscape," a theoretical concept not represented in reality in any populated area [*1*:171–74]. Further it is argued in the same work that we do not study "the nonhuman world" in terms of "natural elements in their inherent characteristics" but only in terms of "natural conditions as significant to man" [*1*:305].

OBJECTIONS TO THE DICHOTOMY

If it is the role of geography to analyze all the kinds of interrelations among the diverse factors whose total interrelationship forms the existing reality of any area, the insistence on distinguishing between two particular groups of factors, human and nonhuman, introduces a number of handicaps to progress in research.

1. In seeking to separate all the factors involved in any areal integration into these two categories, the student is forced to begin his analysis at what may be the most difficult step, a step which could be undertaken only at the most refined level of investigation and in many cases may not be possible even at this level. The first step in analysis is to break down the complexity of all that is within an area into readily recognizable composite features existing in some degree of interrelation with each other, as, for example, vegetation and soil, transportation and waterways, urban structures and the landforms on which they stand. If it were universally, or even generally, true that each such feature was a composite of exclusively human factors or of exclusively natural factors, it would be in order to classify these features in the two groups. We would then be concerned with relationships between human and natural features only at the first level of investigation, whereas the analysis of the integrations of each of the composite features would be concerned only with interrelations among natural factors or among human factors. If it proved not to be feasible to carry through these more refined steps of analysis, whether for lack of time, inadequate data, or inability to determine the intimate process of relationships involved, the description of the relationships between human and natural features at the first level of investigation would remain at least approximately valid.

Undoubtedly this is the manner in which much research in geography has been done. But this is in direct disregard of reality, which recognizes no distinction between "human" and "natural." As Allix, among others, has emphasized [49:296], the features which we commonly think of as "natural" are found by investigation to have been produced by nature and man together; and likewise, features commonly considered as of human origin may be found to have been the product of interactions of human and natural factors in some past time. As Hettner put it, as early as 1905: *Zur Eigenart der Länder gehören Natur und Mensch und zwar in so enger Verbindung dass sie nicht von einander getrennt werden können* ("Both nature and man are intrinsic to the particular character of the areas, and indeed in such intimate union that they cannot be separated from each other") [2:126, from *11*: 554; similarly, Herbertson, 7:149].

2. When the study of the diverse features in interrelation in areas is dominated by the concern to distinguish natural from human factors, the student may easily overlook human factors, particularly invisible ones, which may be of major importance in the particular situation. The "natural factors" are generally readily observable, and most of them at least are included in a relatively short list which geographers commonly carry in their heads; a corresponding check list of human factors is far more difficult to handle.

This problem is reflected, but not solved, when students whose thinking is based on this dichotomy stress "the importance of the cultural factor," as though it were a new thought. In reducing to the singular what is actually a host of factors in part interrelated but in part independent of each other, the expression reflects the dominating concern to determine the importance of natural factors.

3. The recognition of the importance of "cultural factors" introduces a basic confusion in a geographic analysis dominated by a theoretical contrast between human and natural factors. Scientific analysis in general consists of describing the manner in which a particular phenomenon is related to certain other phenomena, or, if one will, in seeking to determine what causal factors produce the known effect. Clear analysis requires sharp separation between the two sides of the statement. If, at the same time, we are required to separate human and nonhuman elements, the combination of the two requirements forces the presumption that they correspond—that is, that human features are to be studied as effects of natural causes. If, however, we recognize that "cultural factors" play a causal role in this relationship, we must place them on the "causative" side along with the "natural causes," and our statement no longer divides the human factors from the nonhuman factors.

To escape from this logical difficulty, many writers exercise tricky footwork with words without realizing that they have thereby lost their original footing. Starting with the concept of "nature" as the "natural environment," shortened for convenience simply to "environment," they then observe that writers in other fields use the latter word to include many things which the geographer does not recognize in the "natural environment," but which are clearly important in the total environment of any individual or human group.

More than one geographer who defines his subject in terms of the mutual relations between man and his natural environment has borrowed from the historian or sociologist the view that "ideas" are a part of the environment, but, failing to note the change he has introduced into the meaning of his term, continues to suppose that he is studying the relations between man and nature.[2]

4. An important practical consequence of the presumption that human features are normally considered as effects in human geography and natural features as causes is the failure to develop in systematic geography the relations of certain human features as causal factors in areas, although their relations as effects may be considered in detail. Three examples may be noted.

Geographers have long studied railroads as resultant features related to the conditions of distance, terrain, resources, and potential production, relations that are no doubt significant and interesting. Far more complex and significant to man, however, are the relations of railroads as *causal* factors affecting a wide variety of features in the areas they traverse—not merely as lines of track, but also as corporate organizations charging rates for traffic not solely dependent on distance and other physical elements.

Only recently, as Allix observes, have we recognized the fundamental and enduring importance of the *cadaster,* the individual landholding, as a determinant of far-reaching effect on agricultural practices, settlements, and the whole economy of an area [49:299]. Prunty's study of the continued importance of this factor in the South (*Geographical Review,* October 1955) has opened a new line of thought in American geography. More generally, as

[2] Numerous examples of such confusion of terms are given in the thorough discussion of this topic by Harold and Margaret Sprout [117:11–17].

Gottmann and Le Lannou both assert, we have failed to recognize the basic importance, as causal factors, of deeply entrenched social facts [56:3ff.; 59:243].

Trewartha has recently stressed our failure to develop a systematic study of one of the more important causative factors in geography—population [119]. We have, of course, not forgotten population in geographic study. But we have assumed that since it was a human feature, its logical place in systematic geography came at the end of the study of human features, as a final effect. Natural conditions permit such and such kinds of economic production, and on this basis population will be dense or sparse. One is reminded of Huntington's classic error in referring to a denser population in the rich Kentucky Bluegrass as compared with the poor mountain area of eastern Kentucky.

In China, India, Puerto Rico, and numerous other areas of the world one dominating feature of the geography is the simple fact that there are so many people there. Starting from this fact, one may, if he chooses, attempt to analyze through many past centuries the processes that have made this possible. But for an understanding of all other aspects of human geography, and indeed of many features in these countries that are commonly classified as natural, one must proceed in the opposite direction, to show the causal relations of this fact of population to such features as soils, size of farms and production per capita, of savings and purchasing power in relation to industrial development, and every other aspect of human geography.

5. No research in geography can hope to make a complete investigation of all the interrelationships of the diverse factors. To disentangle completely the human and nonhuman elements in a particular situation, the student may need to dig back through centuries of human history, even to times earlier than recorded history. But if the study is made with the purpose of determining the relation between human and natural factors, no sound conclusions can be drawn until the study is complete, which will generally be impossible. Hence, even studies of relatively simple elementary problems can yield only hypotheses of low reliability. Successively more penetrating investigations reveal errors in the preceding studies, but do not establish a greater degree of reliabil-

ity, since they likewise introduce, even at the elementary level, uncertainties of their own.

Thus the accumulation of studies carried on by geographers under the "environmentalist" concept did not progress toward increasing approximations of accuracy and certainty. The most that could be said of more thorough studies was that they appeared more convincing, but one knew that later still more thorough research might appear to demonstrate entirely different conclusions.

If, in contrast, we recognize the fundamental rule of science of starting with observation of the naively given phenomena, we know that in geography these, the earth features, are neither purely human nor purely natural, but composite in character. We must begin, then, by considering these earth features, as we find them, as element-complexes distinct from each other, whether composed of human or nonhuman elements or both. The first step is to describe these features according to their characteristics as significant to man and to seek to establish the interrelations among them.

Thus a geographer studying an area in China may accept the existing soil as a single factor to be measured in terms of its present composition, without attempting to unravel the determinants —bedrock, climate, vegetation, insects, *and man*—that have made it what it is [cf. De Jong, 34:33]. Likewise he can accept the existing character and pattern of surface waters without attempting to unravel the degree to which men over the centuries have altered its original features. In analyzing relationships of these existing features to crops, farms, roads, and villages, he can work with the assurance that he knows what he is talking about and can evaluate the degree to which his findings, at whatever level of analysis he is working, are complete, accurate, and certain.

He may find that his analysis, say, of the relation of village location to other features, will not be complete unless he digs back into past conditions. Ultimately he will reach problems that are either insoluble or for which he can offer only very uncertain hypotheses. But, however incomplete his study may be, he will have accomplished the purpose of increasing our comprehension of the place under study, and to the extent that his analysis of the relationships between existing features has been sound, he will have established a base from which later students may be able to advance.

THE SOURCE OF THE PROBLEM—ENVIRONMENTALISM

Although some of these objections to the emphasis on the theoretical dichotomy between man and nature were stated in *The Nature of Geography,* I have never, to my knowledge, been taken to task for insisting that this division is essential in geography. The argument in support is based on the conventional division between the natural and social sciences, a division which elsewhere in the same volume is described as "arbitrary" and a "distortion" of reality [*1*:368].

The statement could, however, have been justified on the basis of current practice—and no doubt that was the basis for this firm conviction and the reason why it has not been attacked by my colleagues. At that time nearly all American geographers used this distinction as basic to their thinking in geography. No doubt most of them still do, though it is worthy of note that it is either not included or plays little role in several of the chapters of *American Geography: Inventory and Prospect* of 1954 [*4*].

To understand why American and British geographers of a decade or so ago accepted without question the emphasis on this abstract dichotomy, we need only look to the immediately preceding period. Practically all of us had been trained in the "environmentalist" concept of geography, in which the distinction between human and natural was fundamental. Although we have abandoned the environmentalist concept,[3] vestiges remain in our thinking. As long as we continue to consider "relationships" in

[3] The objections to this concept, as raised by German students at the turn of the century, and later by Michotte in Belgium and by Sauer and others in this country, are summarized in Section III C of *The Nature of Geography.* (On the wording of the title of this section see footnote 5, in Chapter II of this book.) The concept had also been criticized in England by Forde and E. G. R. Taylor [*1*:xxxii], more recently by Fisher [*70*], Clark [*65*], and Garnier [*73*]. In France it has been subjected to thoroughgoing attack by Le Lannou [*59*:59–90]. The unfortunate consequences for geography of the continued belief among other social scientists that the function of geography is to study the influences of the natural environment are well considered by Platt [*110*] and the Sprouts [*117*:35–38].

geography as synonymous with man-nature relationships, to talk of "the imprint of Man on Land" and "the effect of Land on Man," or to speak of "geographical conditions" as distinct from "economic conditions" [*93*:26–32], we justify Spate's sharp reminder that one cannot escape the problems of environmentalism merely by omitting the concept from the definition of the subject and by omitting the word from our discussions of it [*89*:15].

The core problem of environmentalism is "geographical determinism." A study of the relation of man to his natural environment is obviously incomplete if it does not attempt to answer the question as to what degree the works of man are determined by the conditions of the natural environment. Ratzel and Semple, and those of their followers who have been accused of extreme claims for "determinism," must be credited with having sought a scientific goal. We can escape censure for asserting undemonstrable theories but we can hardly claim scientific quality if we are content with a statement of purpose so vaguely worded as to direct us to study relationships between nature and man without the obligation of attempting to measure those relationships.[4]

The most common alternative to "determinism" is "possibilism," a term which stems apparently from Febvre, based on the viewpoint of Vidal de la Blache [*3*:151]. Although the master of French geography, and his followers since, drew inspiration primarily from Ratzel and emphasized the importance in geography of man-nature relationships, their substantive work was far less dominated by this viewpoint than that in English-speaking countries under the influence of Semple's rendition of the master.[5]

[4] Wooldridge and East suggest that "it is only those geographers who choose to assume the role of amateur word-splitters who will trip persistently in traps of their own making over the word 'determine.'" We need merely recognize "that in a limited or qualified sense an element of determinism remains inevitable in geography, at least in its mode of expression." Consideration of several specific instances leads to the conclusion that "the human, reacting upon the physical circumstances, may be fairly said to 'determine' geographical pattern." This appears to add little to what is referred to in the same discussion as "the comfortable formula that the reactions of Man and Land are mutual," of which the writers observe that "this is evidently true without being either profound or useful" [*93*:32–34].

[5] Neither Ratzel nor Semple supposed that the natural environment was all-determinant, as might possibly be inferred from statements in *The Nature of Geography* [*1*:121f.]. In the preface to her most influential work, *Influences of*

Further, as a student of history, Vidal felt it necessary to emphasize, more so than Ratzel, the elements of uncertainty in the man-
nature relationship that result from differences of cultures, *genres
de vie,* as well as from decisions of individual men. Hence the
concept that nature does not determine what men do, but does
determine a limited number of possibilities from which men may
select [cf. Le Lannou, *58*:274f.; and Allix, *49*:300].

The increased interest in the methodology of geography in recent decades has led to a vigorous debate, among those who adhere
to the "environmentalist" concept, between "determinists" and
"possibilists."[6] Seen from the sidelines, the debate seems both unreal and futile. As Montefiore and Williams conclude, since "both
Possibilists and latter-day Determinists agree that crude environmentalism is dead, there can be no further point in continuing a
dispute which has virtually no bearing on their activities as working geographers" [*84*:11]. Indeed, when one observes how little
fruit has been garnered from a debate which has disturbed geographic thought for more than half a century, one is tempted to
cry "a plague o' both your houses." It is necessary, however, to
consider what light this debate throws on the question discussed
in this chapter—the presumed need to distinguish in geography
between two abstract groups of factors, human and natural.

Geographical Environment, Semple emphasized that "the writer speaks of
geographic factors and influences, shuns the word geographic determinant and
speaks with extreme caution of geographic control." Following Ratzel, she
devoted a chapter to the movements of peoples and cultures (Chapter IV),
and a chapter to location as "the supreme geographic fact in the history of a
country or people" (Chapter V and page 128). She also stressed the importance of past history (page 2) and of previous habitat (pp. 24–25), and emphasized the concept of "the earth as a unit from earliest human time" (pp.
30–31). Tatham, however, finds that passages selected at random demonstrate
a tendency to emphasize the determinant influence of the natural environment [*3*:143–47]. *The Nature of Geography* errs specifically in stating that
Semple maintained only the procedure which Ratzel used in his first volume,
leading from natural causes to human consequences [*1*:91]. Semple also used
the procedure Ratzel followed in his second volume in studying culture in relation to nature.

[6] Tatham has presented an excellent abstract of this debate, which is still
nearly up to date, in his chapter on "Environmentalism and Possibilism"
[*3*:128–62]. The most thoroughgoing critiques have been published subsequently by Montefiore and Williams [*84*], philosopher and geographer, re-
spectively, and by Harold and Margaret Sprout, who have worked both in
political science and in geography [*117*].

E

In fact, all geographers, whatever beliefs they may assert, recognize that we could not possibly explain human choices and actions solely in terms of relationships with the natural environment—that different peoples in identical environments may do different things. Ratzel and Semple stated this directly and Tatham has shown that Griffith Taylor's "stop-and-go determinism" is merely a special form of possibilism [*3*:150f., 161].

But while the validity of "possibleness" is irrefutable, what are we offered by this "wishy-washy term," as E. G. R. Taylor dubs it [*87*:425]? Taken literally, it apparently means that geography, while proclaiming itself as the science primarily concerned with the study of the relationships between man and nature, need only demonstrate in any given situation how the natural conditions made possible one of several, or innumerable, human or social resultants; it need not seek to establish in what manner and degree these natural conditions determine any particular resultant. This means that we are urged to be content with less than might be learned, which is surely contrary to the purpose of science.

Facing the impossibility of absolute determinism on the one hand and what Kirk calls "the creeping paralysis of possibilism" on the other [*77*:158],[7] geographers who still think of their subject in terms of some form of environmentalism, seek a middle road, such as Spate's concept of "probablism" [*87*:419f.]. More commonly they seek, consciously or unconsciously, to avoid philosophical questions by using everyday expressions—to "explain" or to "account for" human features by correlating them with natural conditions. Scrutinizing such attempts in terms of the logic of systematic social science, the Sprouts demonstrate that they conceal a series of implicit and by no means demonstrable assumptions concerning human motivations and decisions, whether of groups or of individuals [*117*:50–57].

The problem involved in this discussion, complex though it is, is much simpler than that commonly involved in the "environ-

[7] Some years earlier Wooldridge and Linton wrote of "the risk of replacing the crudities of 'Determinism' by the banalities of a formless 'Possibilism,'" in S. W. Wooldridge and David Linton, *Structure, Surface and Drainage in South-East England,* Institute of British Geographers, Publ. No. 10 (1939), p. 124.

mentalist" concept of geography. Looking at the problem from the point of view of social science, the Sprouts are concerned with the relationships between men as individuals or social groups, and the material environment existing at any time, independent of man at that time, but regardless of whether originally man-made or not. This "nonhuman environment" therefore includes not only landforms, soil, rivers, etc., but also fields, buildings, canals, roads, railroads, and machinery [*117*:15]. This realistic concept is quite different from the abstract concept of the natural environment as geographers have generally conceived it, which includes only factors that are independent of the work of man at any time, past as well as present.[8]

If this latter purpose were required of geography, there would be no escape from Martin's challenge of "The Necessity of Determinism" [*82*]—not that we must assume that the natural environment determines absolutely, but that we would be required to seek to measure how far it does determine. However, this would require, as a basic step in analysis, that every feature observed in geographic study must be broken down to disentangle its complex of factors, separating out the purely natural factors from social or individual human factors, no matter how remote in time or space the process relationships involved. Even if we had command of all that is now known by the social sciences and psychology, we would still lack the detailed knowledge of facts and relationships necessary for this essential step in analysis. In short, the environmentalist concept of geography, whether considered in terms of "possibilism" or "probablism," imposes as a necessity what is, in fact, an impossibility.

On the other hand, do we escape this dilemma merely by abandoning the environmentalist concept? Certainly our concern is not "merely to describe," but to study the relationships among the phenomena we observe. Are we not then back where we

---

[8] In attempting to summarize the use, by geographers, of the terms "natural environment" and "nonhuman environment," the Sprouts make several statements to which geographers may take exception. This is not surprising in view of what they rightly term a "semantic tangle" [*117*:14f.]. Neither could they find a clear answer in *The Nature of Geography*, which uses "natural environment" without defining it, merely asserting that "there is very general agreement among geographers as to exactly what it includes" [*1*:172].

started? If this is what Spate means by his challenge [*89*:15], then, surely, he has carried over from the earlier concept the assumption that in geography "relationship" means a relationship between human and natural factors. It is true that any science must start with taxonomy. In geography, we are concerned at an elementary level of classification to recognize mountains, hills, valleys, river courses, levees, etc. But whether a particular hill, river course, or levee is of natural origin or produced by man in some past time is a distinction of secondary importance; if our research is insufficient to determine that distinction, we can nonetheless study its existing relationship to other features (farms, homes, vegetation, etc.).

These considerations lead logically to the conclusion that if the purpose of geography is the search for the most complete description and understanding of the earth as the home of man, we are not required to divide all features or elements of the earth into two categories, those of nature and those of man. Are we, however, free to accept this logical conclusion? Certainly we cannot lightly discard a concept which appears so firmly entrenched in our heritage.

THE PAST COMMITMENT

Originally the concept of a cleavage between man and nature was extraneous to geography. If it entered first as a consequence of the religious teleological viewpoint of Ritter and his followers, it became of major importance, Sauer noted, as a concept of the philosophy of history supported by the rise of natural science, Darwinism, and the rationalist philosophy of the mid-nineteenth century [*24*:24]. More specifically, the apparent demonstration of absolute certainty of law in the physical sciences, and its introduction into the biological sciences, inspired the belief that man, as part of total nature, was likewise controlled by undeviating "natural law." Hence the social sciences also could be free of the necessity of admitting willful vagaries to human decision or any supernatural control.

To establish this faith, however, it was necessary for the social sciences to demonstrate the validity of the doctrine as a scientific theory. This could only be done in dependence on the natural sciences, since man as a part of total nature is obviously dependent upon nature-minus-man, which existed before man and could exist independent of man. Man must therefore be the product of nature-minus-man, dependent on laws operating through nature-minus-man.

While this doctrine affected all the social sciences, the consequences were most far-reaching in geography, because in that field human and nonhuman variables are most intimately intermixed. It may well have seemed logical that since man was the product of nature (nature-minus-man), the study of relationships between them should begin with nature.

Also important, then and now, is the general assumption that because knowledge in the natural sciences is generally more complete and reliable than in the social sciences we are on firmer footing in our knowledge of the natural environment than in that of man and society. Geography, specializing in the study of the natural environment, was therefore called upon to "bridge the gap." Among the several fallacies inherent in this assumption is the failure to recognize that the concept of "environment" is meaningless save in reference to that which is environed. When we actually come to an examination of the processes in relationships between man and natural factors, we find that we do not know what elements of nature need to be examined until we have a thorough knowledge of psychological and social reactions. In other words, we cannot start with nature, but rather must first analyze human and social processes, as in the social sciences, before we can think of the relationships to nature.

If this conclusion escaped the attention of most workers in the social sciences, there were nonetheless those who recognized that thorough analysis and explanation of the phenomena they studied required study of the relation between those phenomena and particular natural factors. While some might stop at that point because of ignorance of the natural factors involved, those willing to secure the necessary knowledge could not be persuaded that they were entering the field of geography.

Very often, however, they found that geographers had worked on such problems "from the other side," but commonly with no systematic attempt to develop a field. Under the doctrine of environmental influences this was not necessary. To establish the validity of that doctrine, any aspect of human life, at any time or place, was equally open to study. Geographers therefore could, and did, carry out innumerable scattered excursions into other fields [1:124–26]. That this viewpoint continues to influence work in geography is demonstrated by the frequent identification of the adjective "geographical" as synonymous with "physical" or "natural." More specifically, it is illustrated in the wide range of topics which Wooldridge and East consider as appropriately included within geography, under "the right or the hope of making contributions from the geographical side" to economics or political science [93:124, 143f.].[9]

Whether such studies are designed to demonstrate some degree of "geographic determinism" or merely "the importance of geographic factors," the motivating purpose of the study constitutes a subjective influence on the conclusions. This is expressed in the writings of many who think in terms of nature-man relationships by the personification of nature, as Spate and the Sprouts have observed [87:419; 89:28f.; 117:34]. In place of the religious teleology of Ritter, which is denounced,[10] the disciples of the new "objective" philosophy have substituted a no less omnipotent, even omniscient, Nature, dominated throughout by mechanistic laws. "Nature's plan is obvious," writes Griffith Taylor; man's part is to study "the character of the environment . . . so that he can best follow the plan 'determined' by nature" [3:16]. Philosophically speaking, one might wonder why it should be considered more "rational" to presume planning by nature, which so far as

---

[9] Hence they conclude that it would be "a foolish and retrograde step to force geography too straitly into the procrustean bed of 'areal differentiation' " [93:144]. In other words, although they first accept Hettner's position as providing a "philosophically rational" program, the modification then added—that geography concerns Land and Man and the relations between them—is the dominating concept [93:26f.]. This is but one of numerous examples of the attempts to combine the concept of modern German geographers with the inherited environmentalist concept to which it is opposed.

[10] Griffith Taylor emphasizes his disapproval of Ritter's teleological concept by calling it "theocratic," and also by erroneously labelling Ritter as a "historian," significant in geography merely as one of "the disciples of Humboldt" [3:5]. In the following chapter of the same volume, which Taylor edited, Tatham presents well-documented statements concerning Ritter and his work [3:42–48].

we can observe it is unthinking, than by a divine being presumed to be rational.

In the meantime, however, the philosophy of science, which environmentalist geographers sought to demonstrate, has lost its original foundation. The most nearly exact sciences no longer assume that the phenomena they study are subject to explanation in terms of undeviating scientific laws. It is a curious consequence, as Montefiore and Williams observe, that in an effort to attain respectability for geography as a science, environmentalists should continue "a metaphysical dispute of a type which modern positivistically minded philosophers at any rate would call the very reverse of respectable" [*84*:9f.].

Whatever may have been the case a century ago, geography is under no obligation to science in general to distinguish among the factors interrelated in the phenomena it studies between those of human origin and those of natural origin. Neither is it committed by its own past. While the published works of geographers of the environmentalist school contain descriptions of places and studies of specific relationships among phenomena which have lasting value, their attempts to demonstrate a general thesis of relationship between man and nature have produced no secure building blocks useful for more advanced study. Nothing is lost by abandoning trails which offer no possibility of progressive advance. Fortunately, many geographers who repeat, in occasional methodological utterances or in introductions to substantive works, the concept of geography as the study of relationships between man and nature pay little attention to that dictum in their actual studies.

CONCLUSION

The earth shell which forms the subject of study in geography is a composite of varying integrations of a multiplicity of diverse phenomena interrelated in a great variety of ways. From the point of view of other sciences, or of philosophy, it is useful to classify these phenomena in different ways. Geography, in seeking to analyze the complexity of integrated phenomena in reality, is concerned to examine relationships among phenomena, of whatever kinds, which are found to be significant in the total integration. In many cases such relationships may be those between human and nonhuman phenomena, in others between animate (whether human or nonhuman) and inanimate phenomena, or between visible and invisible, or between material and nonmaterial. But no one of these dichotomies is logically of any more significance to geography than any other; in every case it is the particular nature of the phenomena which determines the relationships.

Geography, however, had forced upon it during a relatively short period of its history a philosophical concept, "environmentalism," under which it was the duty of geography to investigate relationships specifically between human and nonhuman factors, and therefore to divide all elements into those two abstract groups. This concept, however, is extraneous in purpose, prejudicial to sound research, and disruptive of the fundamental unity of the field. We can escape the "problems of environmentalism" by following Humboldt in considering the diverse features and elements of the earth surface without attempting to separate them on either side of that arbitrary, abstract line. In sum, we conclude with Platt, that so far as geography is concerned, "environmentalism appears to have outlived its usefulness, and to require extermination as an obstacle to better understanding" [110:352].

We may hope to secure better understanding by seeking to learn as much as we can of the manner and degree in which the diverse features of an area, and their component elements, are interrelated with each other in determining the total character of areas. In describing and analyzing individual features and elements, we are free to utilize whatever categories of classification are empirically significant to the study of their interrelationships, without concern for the abstract distinction between those of human origin and those of natural origin.

VII.

The Division of Geography
by Topical Fields — The Dualism of
Physical and Human Geography

THE CONCLUSIONS reached in the previous chapter raise a challenge to a division of geography that has been commonly accepted and followed in university courses for decades, as though between two parts each coherent and unified—human geography and non-human geography. It is unfortunate that we have come to call the latter "physical geography," a term which had a quite different meaning for geographers a century or so ago and carries several different meanings in common usage today. Our terminology would be more consistent if, as both Wooldridge and Allix have suggested [92:45; 49:296], we spoke of "natural geography," that is, geography limited to natural features as distinct from those made by man.

One might suppose that a major division on the basis of the kinds of materials studied in a particular field would rest on readily observable distinctions in the naively given facts, and that within each division the categories of facts studied would be more nearly similar, in contrast to the greater differences between those in other divisions. Consequently, each division would develop its distinct methods of observation and study.

We have found, however, that even after laborious research by many able scholars it may not be possible to separate features of the earth resulting from nature exclusive of man from those that result primarily from man. Moreover, the division fails to meet

the second criterion: each half contains highly heterogeneous categories requiring a variety of methods of observation, whereas
there is a close similarity between cultivated crops studied in one
half and wild vegetation studied in the other. Schlüter indeed asserted that "the transition from the physical to the human part of
the science involves no greater jump than from climate to landforms, or from landforms to the vegetative cover" [*1*:213]; if this
be considered an exaggeration, it nonetheless emphasizes the very
great differences in character among the several nonhuman elements.

In contrast, everyone recognizes that the atmospheric elements
form a single category, climate, requiring methods of study peculiar to itself. Much the same is true of each of the other conventional categories of "natural elements." Few of these, however,
are completely nonhuman; minor landforms, microclimates, soils,
and wild vegetation are all affected to a greater or lesser degree
by human culture. Very often geographers studying these "natural" features have followed the logic of this abstract division to
exclude or ignore the effects of man. The result is to provide a
description not of what exists in reality, but of what is believed
to have existed in the past, even the remote past.

The situation on the opposite side of geography is more obvious: it is absurd on the face of it to think of human geography
as separate from physical geography. Man is of the earth, earthy,
as Ritter emphasized in speaking of *die irdisch erfüllten Räume
der Erdoberfläche* [*1*:142].[1] Every material work of man, whether
a house, implanted in the ground, a farm or a city, represents a
composite of natural and cultural elements.

If there is then no real separation between the physical and
human elements in geography, we do not have a field of two distinct parts, but rather a field in which certain of the features
studied have been presumably in large part determined by nature without man, whereas other features studied have been in
large part determined by man working with nature. Hence Hett-

---

[1] Many a student has been puzzled by the word *irdisch* in Ritter's phrase.
Whatever his reason for using it, he stated explicitly in the context that he
included not only the earth crust (*Erdrinde*), the plant cover, and the animal world, but also the human world in all its activities, including "ani-
mated movements" and "intellectual forces" [*22*:41, 49, 51].

ner, as noted earlier, found nature and man inseparable in the complex union that forms the character of areas. In amplification of this thought, Herbertson wrote in 1916: "We cannot consider . . . an inhabited country apart from its inhabitants without abstracting an essential part of the whole. . . . The separation of the whole into man and his environment is a murderous act. . . . The living whole . . . is no longer the living whole when it is so dissected, but something dead and incomplete" [7:149]. Similarly Vidal de la Blache concluded in a statement often quoted: "Human geography, therefore, is not contrasted with a geography from which human interests have been excluded. Indeed such has never existed except in the minds of specialists" [28:3; cf. Sauer, 25:178; Allix, 49:296; Edwards, 69:89].

In this country discussions in the committee which prepared the volume on *American Geography* led to the conclusion, as expressed both by James and by Whittlesey, that the division between physical and human geography obscured rather than illuminated the true nature of the subject [4:15, 28]. Many, however, were shocked at this suggestion, and subsequent writings have demonstrated that the concept of the study of the "physical earth" is deeply rooted in our thinking. It is necessary, therefore, to consider the historical background of the concept.

HISTORICAL DEVELOPMENT OF THE DUALISM

The very term "physical geography" is one of the most venerable and honored in our field, stemming at least from the time of Varenius and used by Kant and Humboldt. But for those students the word "physical" had a different connotation from that which it has subsequently acquired [1:36, 42f.]. Humboldt took pains to explain that he used the term to suggest a science of laws like physics, that his "physical geography" was directly comparable to the "general geography" of Varenius, which we now call "systematic geography." "The great problem of physical geography [literally, "the physics of the world"] is to determine . . . the laws of these relationships, the eternal bonds that enchain the phenomena of life with those of inanimate nature" [1:76, 79; 14:60, 64].

Physical geography, therefore, for Humboldt as for Kant, included man, not as an afterthought, but as essential to the unity of nature.[2] During the following decades texts called "physical geography" commonly followed Humboldt in including a section on the races of men. Only in the present century has the chapter on "man" dropped out.

More recently a further restriction can be observed, namely, the limitation of "physical" to the inorganic world, and the recognition of a biogeography, the geography of living things—a development which caused Fairgrieve to ask whether the central theme of geography is to be "man versus the rest" or "organic versus inorganic" [*93*:56]. Wooldridge and East raise this question but leave the reader in doubt as to their answer. Perhaps the authors felt the answer to be unimportant: "A division of the subject into 'physical geography' and 'human geography' is a false dichotomy. Such cleavage is the very thing geography exists to bridge, and it is false to its central aim whenever and for whatever reasons it recognizes or emphasizes two 'sides' in the subject" [*93*:28].

This time-honored metaphor, however, destroys the principle in which it is encompassed. The sole purpose of a bridge is to connect two sides of a cleavage; a false dichotomy requires no bridge. Nature, as a whole reality, presents no cleavage between man and nature-minus-man, and until the latter part of the nineteenth century man's study of that reality recognized no such cleavage and therefore no bridge was needed [*1*:369].

Within geography itself the academic division between natural and social split the field into two parts, so that in some universities geographers found themselves in separate faculties. To reunite the two into a single field was the purpose of Mackinder's famous address of 1887 [*16*]. But the concept of geography as a

[2] Humboldt asserted this principle in many of his earlier writings, in letters, in his public lectures of 1827–28, and in several passages in the *Kosmos*, of which the principal one is quoted in full by Tatham [*1*:65, 67–68; *3*:54; *14*: 170, 378]. He did, however, distinguish in his physical geography between the realm of nature, in which man was included as the highest organism, and the realm of the intellect or art—even though he recognized that the distinction was in a sense unreal, *als wäre das Geistige nicht auch in dem Naturganzen enthalten* [*14*:69]. Although his studies of areas included consideration of moral and aesthetic problems, as stated in a passage in *The Nature of Geography* in which that clause is quoted [*1*:67], he did not, as is there implied, include such considerations in his "physical geography" [*14*:386].

bridge tends to perpetuate this dualism within geography. One may call the dichotomy of man and nature false, but if one continues to discuss geography in those terms, the subject inevitably falls apart into a physical and a human, or social, geography.

LACK OF COHERENCE IN "PHYSICAL GEOGRAPHY"

The disunity is more than one of dualism. Any standard text entitled "physical geography" demonstrates Kirk Bryan's conclusion that when considered apart from the rest of geography, "it is a group of special sciences each pursued for its own end," so that there is no coherent unity [99:189]. The same disunity is evident in the theoretical discussion by Wooldridge and East. What elsewhere in the text is called simply "physical geography" as a main division of the field, here falls into two subdivisions, "physical geography and biogeography," and the former falls apart into nearly discrete pieces. While the authors recognize that land, air, and ocean are "in important respects curiously different and separate," they assert, as a "truism," that "the three are intimately linked" [93:41] and seek to support this truism by an assertion of faith:

> . . . There is evidently a sense in which a balanced and compendious picture of lithosphere, hydrosphere and atmosphere, taken together, has a scientific role and value, quite apart from the demand made for it by geographers. Aside altogether from its human aspect, our planet and the inter-relationships of its parts are a unitary subject for study which presents a certain intellectual completeness. . . . The unitary point of view still has its value. . . . Whether we regard our planet as the home of life or as the home of man, the sum total of its intricate physical economy is a fit and necessary background to the study [93:55f.].[3]

These statements are quoted at length because they illustrate so well, to my mind, the essence of the problem. The earth shell

---

[3] The phrase "unitary subject for study" is evidently not to be taken in any literal sense, since it can be either the total of inorganic elements or the total of nonhuman elements. In another essay Wooldridge quotes with approval Fleure's objection to the "deep fission" in geography "into two incomplete and inadequate parts," physical and human [92:19].

which constitutes the only unitary subject with an actually existing sum total of economy is formed of intricately interlocking parts, not only of land, air, and water, but also of plants, animals, and men; fields, fences, barns, and houses; roads, trains, books, and radio sounds. All these animate and man-made features are intricately constructed of varying bits of solid, liquid, and gaseous materials, subtracted from inanimate forms. If then we mentally subtract, from this whole, man and all his works, what remains is something less than the total of inorganic earth; it is a mental abstraction having no coherence in reality [similarly, Humboldt, *14*:367f.].

The concept of "physical geography" as the study of the non-human features of the earth developed at the same time as the concept that the special function of geography was to study relationships between man and the (nonhuman) earth. Both stem from the philosophy of science which, as we noted in the previous chapter, seeks to explain the phenomena of man in terms of nonhuman phenomena, subject to natural laws. The task of "physical geography," therefore, was to study "the physical environment of man."

Leighly has recently voiced his objection to this subordination of physical geography to the study of the natural factors as the causal half of the environmentalist dogma.[4] To escape from the limitations thus imposed, Leighly proposes that physical geography should exclude all consideration of human use and seek simply "to trace the operations of the laws of nature upon the earth" in "the land, the sky and the water" [*108*:318]. But surely, what we observe in the land, the water, and even in the sky, are the resultants of interaction of many elements including, in varying degree, human as well as nonhuman elements. To trace the operation of the laws of nonhuman nature upon the earth is to pursue an intellectual abstraction, which on the one hand disrupts the actual unity of all terrestrial elements and on the other

[4] The general philosophical roots of this view of physical geography are stated briefly in Leighly's paper, but more attention is paid to the particular role which William Morris Davis and. later students are said to have played [*108*:309–17]. Robert S. Platt published a criticism of Leighly's views in "A Note on Rollin D. Salisbury," *Annals*, Association of American Geographers, Vol. XLVII (1957) , 276.

hand does not by itself form a partial unity, an integrated part of the whole.

In contrast, the concept of the "natural environment" appeared to geographers of a generation or so ago to give a certain form of unity to physical geography. They forgot that the term itself is only a collective name for individual elements and element-complexes which can be integrated only in terms of what is being environed.

Geographers in France, according to Le Lannou, have come to much the same conclusion: "Il y a longtemps que nous avons répudié le mythe du 'milieu naturel', absolument privé de sens dans notre discipline" [59:234f.]. Le Lannou likewise rejects Cholley's classification of three kinds of milieux—physical, biological, and human [52:21–25]. The issue here, however, hinges perhaps on semantic distinctions. Cholley does not speak of a physical milieu, or a biological milieu, but in each case in terms of plurals—milieux. Further, he uses the term not in our sense of "environment," but rather of "area," or "type of area." In this sense, then, Cholley speaks of a climatic milieu, a soil milieu, a geomorphological milieu, etc., but these together do not form one "physical milieu," but rather many "physical milieux." Each of these, however, represents only a particular aspect of an area, divorced from the total. As Le Lannou emphasizes, there is in reality but one milieu as an actual entity, which he would call the *geographic milieu,* the total of all interrelated phenomena of the area [58: 275–77; 59:91ff.].

SYSTEMATIC DIVISION OF HUMAN GEOGRAPHY

Just as we have followed the systematic natural sciences in grouping predominantly natural features into fields by categories, we have followed the standard divisions of the social sciences in establishing systematic fields of human geography. It is in order to consider whether such a division into segments defined in abstract terms—economic, political, and sociological—corresponds to the purpose and needs of geography.

Since transportation is an economic activity, we have commonly included it as a segment of the field of economic geography. But as Ullman has noted, the movement of goods, people, and ideas across areas is an essential part of every aspect of human geography. The geography of circulation—the term used in France to include both transportation and communication—is a distinctive field of geography which is likely to be handled in unbalanced manner when considered simply as part of economic geography [4:311].

Similarly, in including urban geography as part of economic geography, we tend to regard a city as "an economic phenomenon, with associated social and political attributes" [4:143]; one could say the same of man in general. Geographically, cities are distinctive as areas where space is almost fully occupied by all kinds of human activities and associated structures and institutions, other than those of primary production. A major part of the space indeed is occupied for living purposes other than economic.

If we consider the aspects of geography that are predominantly concerned with the work of man, do these form together a unified and coherent field? The Committee on American Geography originally planned its volume on this assumption, but was led to conclude that economic geography must be treated as "a group of fields" rather than as a single field of research. Because of the different procedures of analysis used in its different aspects, "economic geography tends more and more to break into component topical specialties" [4:241].

Those who, like myself,[5] have attempted to organize this field, whether for teaching or research, will recognize the problems which led to that conclusion. Among the great variety of topics considered in the geography of agriculture there is a major common thread of production of biotic products from the soil, and hence a common integration of a certain range of human activities with the elements of soil, climate, slope of the land, drainage, etc. But between the geography of agriculture and that of mineral production, or between either of these and the geography of manufacturing, there are great discontinuities with relatively few interconnections. To say that all are concerned "with man's means of gaining a livelihood" is to express an abstract rather than

---

[5] Prior to 1940 I had taught a course in economic geography during more than forty quarters and had published articles in that field [1:18, 19].

a concrete similarity. There is little of common character in the activities of clerks in offices and stores of a modern city and those of tribesmen gathering wild products and cultivating patches of land.

There is, however, one aspect of man's economy which would provide the basis for a unitary segment of geography—namely, the geography of consumption. This, as Allix has emphasized, is a form of areal variation over the earth, and within different parts of individual countries, of greatest significance for all of geography [49:296]. To relate such a field to the many essentially separate geographies of production, we need to develop far more than we have the geography of exchange, including marketing as well as transportation.

Even if we envisage a future development of such an integrated field, we must recognize that, in the portion concerned with production, it will consist of several sections, each of which is largely independent of the others in its closest integrations, and these involve different sets of features for each section: agricultural production with soil and climate, mineral production very specifically with mineral deposits, and manufacturing primarily with spatial connections of a variety of still other factors. Hence, the geographer who specializes in agricultural geography has more in common with those who specialize in the geography of soils or of climate than with one specializing in the geography of manufacturing; but our conventional division puts the first topic with the last, in economic geography, in contrast to the others, which are included in physical geography.

INDUCTIVE CONSTRUCTION OF TOPICAL FIELDS IN GEOGRAPHY

Our examination of the consequences of dividing geography on the basis of categories similar to those of the systematic sciences brings us back, in each case, to the concept repeatedly expressed in the writings of Humboldt and Ritter of the indivisible unity of all earth features. However, this does not mean that the geographer can only look at the whole "as a whole." To comprehend how it forms a whole over the entire world, and a total complex at any one place, he must find ways of concentrating on particu-

F

lar kinds of features, studying their interrelations among themselves and their relations with other features, in order to understand the total integrations existing in reality.

The naively given facts with which we are presented are not main divisions of earth features, but a host of individual features —rainfall, surface slope, trees, men, rivers, roads, houses, factories, industrial corporations, economic systems, states, cultures, etc. Since the list is almost unlimited, we must devise some useful method of organizing this multiplicity of features into a manageable system. In contrast to the sciences concerned with particular categories of phenomena, geography is concerned with these features not in themselves but as elements in areal integration; hence, we need to analyze such features in their component parts only to the extent that such analysis is necessary for the comprehension of their interrelations with other features.

We actually start, as Bobek and Schmithüsen have pointed out, with a large number of element-complexes whose composition or internal integration does not vary areally [29:116]. Thus we accept from the systematic sciences the composition of the atmosphere or the individual integrations of plants and animals.

The integrations which geography is concerned to analyze are those which vary from place to place. The organization of our work will be most effective if we group together the phenomena which we find to be most commonly interrelated; analysis of such segments, as partial integrations of the contents of area, will enable us to take the biggest steps toward comprehension of the total integration of area.

Recent studies by German geographers of the problem of regional division follow in part an inductive approach by starting with individual elements or element-complexes and building successively higher levels of integration.[6] They assume, however, that these levels correspond to the categories of inorganic, organic, and social. The inorganic features in the earth surface (not including,

---

[6] A large number of German geographers working in teams in the field and following a common plan mapped the regional division of Germany into *Naturräume* (literally, "natural areas," but only in terms of a somewhat unusual concept of the word "natural"). The theoretical basis for this project has been presented in papers by Otremba [39], and Schmithüsen [42 and 43] and by Bobek and Schmithüsen [29], and discussed by Carol [32] and Uhlig [48].

it would appear, mineral resources) "exist in manifold relations with each other," forming a "total inorganic complex, which in comparison with the individual features presents a new and higher level of areal integration" [29:116] But the exposition makes clear that these features are not integrated in themselves but only in terms of their significance for organic features, whether the natural (rather, "wild") vegetation or the productive use by man [42:9; 39:157]. The latter criterion, as Otremba recognizes, necessitates the addition of location as a factor.

The resultant maps and descriptions should be highly useful in presenting in organized form a collection of factual information concerning each of the many small areas of Germany. But in terms of methodology it merely demonstrates that such features as elevation, relief, soil, waters, and climate, though in various ways interrelated, are in very important respects independent of each other and so form only a very weak degree of integration. They are integrated in considerably greater degree, but still only partially, by vegetation, and more fully only by the hand of man. In short, the deductive categories of inorganic, organic, and human (or "intellectual") are not geographically useful.

It may help us to surmount this obstacle to our thinking if we observe that within the individual branches of geography that have established coherent unity, such as geomorphology, we have not adhered to these theoretical distinctions. The study of landforms, in the proper sense of configuration of the earth surface, is not restricted to one type of material, and cannot be successfully divided by types of materials, inorganic and organic, solid and liquid. To follow the latter scheme, as some texts in fact do, is to divorce rivers from valleys in order to add them to the oceans—that is, rivers are mere conduits to the sea. But since deformation of the solid surface cannot be explained without consideration of running water, rivers appear in the discussion of landforms merely as tools of erosion and deposition. One is given little or no concept of waters as an integral and important part of the surface forms of the land, or of the functional organization of river systems, one of the more remarkable products of nature, each unique and significant in its particular pattern. Fortunately for students, atlas maps continue to portray these individual systems.

The clearest case of acceptance in our standard system of the integration of elements of quite different categories is in the study of soils. In this case we do not place the inorganic and organic components in separate topical fields; we recognize that earth worms are important to geography because of their functional relation to soils rather than because of their organic similarity to trees or elephants. But thanks to the dogma that nature and man must be considered separately, our study of the geography of soils still lacks adequate consideration of the effects of human cultivation.

These cases should not be considered as exceptional but rather as examples reminding us that any system of division of the indivisible terrestrial unity is arbitrary, cutting through actual interrelations. For the purpose of geography, a topical division will be least disruptive if it recognizes both the degree of integration as well as the degree of similarity of phenomena. Topics should be so organized as to include in each the maximum degree of integration of elements of a minimum number of different categories. Each topical division should contain a greater number of close interrelations internally than of relations with features in other topical divisions.

Mineral deposits present a particularly clear example. They play little or no role in any integration in which man is not included, for they are "resources" only for man. Furthermore, the correlation between the human phenomena involved in extracting them and the deposits is an absolute one, in one direction: coal mining is carried on only where coal deposits occur. Relationships with other earth features—whether landforms, climate, or soil—are only of either local or incidental importance. Hence, it seems peculiarly arbitrary that in many texts the discussion of mineral industries and mineral deposits should be separated by hundreds of pages, or even placed in separate volumes. Geographically speaking, they form a closely integrated group of phenomena, together with the distinctive social phenomena of mining communities [*1*:221].

A very different, but likewise closely integrated element of areal variation is based on the dominating influence of the ocean on all its contents, whether inorganic or organic. Such a topical segment may well also include the activity of man in harvesting produce from the sea by fishing, sealing, or whaling, although these activities necessarily overlap into topics studying coastal land areas.

Far more complex is the closely interwoven segment of elements associated with the agricultural activities of cultivated areas. Analysis of these must include not only areal variations in conditions of climate, soil, slope, and drainage, but also of systems of land tenure and holdings, consumption habits, and numerous other factors of cultural heritage. Furthermore, such a topical study may well include processing industries which are closely interwoven in the rural agricultural life, whether located in farmyards, at crossroads, or in village plants. The same is true of the distinctive institutions and organizations of rural social life.

It is true, of course, that if one follows this inductive method in organizing a study into topical segments, certain features will appear as significant in several topics. Landforms are importantly related to transportation, agriculture, and the location of urban industries. But the relationships are of different character in each case. Likewise, the relationships between climatic conditions on the one hand and agriculture, transportation, or human physiology on the other depend on different characteristics of the climate —indeed, this is true in respect to different kinds of agricultural production. It may be desirable in research study, or in student training, to concentrate for a time on climate as an element in the integration of phenomena varying through area, but one must avoid considering climate in isolation, analyzing "climate for its own sake"—whatever that may mean.[7] Rather it is necessary to analyze and assess the characteristics which are significant in their areal variation to the diverse phenomena with which they are significantly related.

Since the differences in the several climatic elements which are most significant in one form of integration, say in agriculture in northwestern Europe, are not the most significant in another, say in transportation in northwestern United States, we should

---

[7] The study of the atmosphere as an object is the subject of meteorology. "Climate" is the sum of certain characteristics of the atmosphere which vary areally in significant relation to some other phenomena, that is, the term implies environment, though not necessarily in reference to man.

not expect any standard system of classification of climatic elements to be generally useful. Beyond the simplest level of reconnaisance description, or the most elementary level of teaching, we would need a different system of classification of climates for each of a large number of diverse topics. Whether there is actual need for any system of classification of the sum of climatic characteristics is another question. Since climatic qualities are measured in single arithmetic figures, it is not clear that "types" or "classes" of climate defined in terms of brackets of those figures are more useful in research than the specific figures themselves.

The approach to topical organization of geography in terms of segments of partial integration, each consisting of some variety of closely interwoven elements, will unquestionably produce a division of geography in which each topical sector overlaps many of the others. This, we repeat, is inevitable in the nature of the subject. The relevant question is whether such a system provides successively increasing integration, with the minimum of duplication. We do not eliminate that by attempting to divide the heterogeneous phenomena of geography into discrete sections each of similar kinds. Since our purpose in geography is not the study of the phenomena themselves, but of phenomena in interrelation with other and different phenomena, no matter what the basis of division, each sector will include interrelations with others; duplication is inevitable.

It is also true that this approach will not lead to a single standard system of topical division of geography. This is also consistent with the nature of the subject. Looking at the earth from different viewpoints, one may wish to concentrate on any of a number of different groupings of partial integrations. Examination of the literature, other than that of textbooks, would demonstrate, I believe, that geographers have been most successful when they exercised this freedom in combining elements inductively rather than in following the conventional divisions of systematic geography.

There is, however, one method of dividing the field deductively which corresponds in considerable degree to segments of integration arrived at inductively. In terms of close relationships of a large number of the variable factors of areas, the earth surface is divided into five major classes, each having its distinct association of features: (1) the oceans; (2) the areas of permanent ice, whether on sea or land; (3) the land areas of predominantly wild vegetation and animal life, uncontrolled though perhaps markedly altered by man [1:337f., 348]; (4) the "rural" areas, controlled and used by man for production from the soil; and (5) urban areas. The fact that these types of areas are recognized in common thought and speech as contrasts of the first order is in itself a form of inductive perception of distinctive segments of integration.

Certain major features, notably climate, landforms, and social heritage, overlap most or all of these types of areas, but their relationships with other elements are notably distinct in each type. Areas of different types are also interconnected, primarily through the work of man, so that there is also need for topical studies of the phenomena, primarily those of human institutions, which produce areal integrations extending over all five types of areas.

CONCLUSION

The traditional organization of geography by topics into two halves, "physical" and "human," and the division of each half into sectors based on similarity of the dominant phenomena in each, is of relatively recent origin and has proven detrimental to the purpose of geography—the comprehension of the integrations of phenomena of diverse character which fill areas in varying ways over the earth. It did not arise from internal need in geography, but from a philosophical abstraction which attempted to separate man from the rest of nature and from the concern of the systematic sciences to study categories of phenomena as much as possible in isolation from each other.

The consideration of categories of phenomena which are largely independent of man facilitates the construction and application of "natural laws." With the increasing prestige of the "natural sciences," particularly the "physical sciences," many geographers were stimulated to concentrate on the nonhuman aspects of their field and to construct courses and textbooks called "physical geography." Such collections of knowledge concerning particular categories of earth features, however scientific in quality, were lacking in coherence and divorced from the full context of reality; in consequence they had only limited appeal to the general student. At the same time the study of the human aspects of geography, in large part divorced from the physical earth features with which they are in reality interwoven, lost both scientific standing and student interest. The disastrous consequences for the status of geography in the secondary schools is well known.

Geography can expect to compete for interest with the systematic sciences only if it recognizes in all its branches its own distinctive purpose, namely, to observe and analyze earth features composed of the interrelations of diverse elements with each other. While some of these features are largely independent of man and others are the product of man's work, few are either purely "natural" or purely "human." They could be distributed along a continuum from one to the other, but there is no gain for geography in establishing such differences. In studying the interrelations of earth features, geography analyzes those features to the extent necessary to explain their interrelations, regardless of whether these interrelations can be described in terms of "natural laws" or "social laws."

For this purpose, specialization by topics is necessary in geography as in any other field of study, but that specialization will be most fruitful if based on associated phenomena, however heterogeneous, that are most commonly found in close interrelationship. Each special field in geography may therefore contribute its share to the understanding of a particular group of partial integrations, which can be built up into a more nearly complete comprehension of the total integration whose variations over the earth constitute the subject matter of geography.

From the point of view of sound development of the field, and also of contributing to the students' comprehension of the world in which they live, it is unfortunate that the college faculties and course requirements are arbitrarily divided between the "natural sciences" and the "social sciences," and each of these is divided by categories of similar phenomena. To establish our proper place in the over-all educational function, we need to impress on our faculties and administrators the distinctive value which, as Hettner and Schlüter observed, geography can offer in reuniting our cultural life, which now tends to fall apart in diverging directions [2:127; *1*:213].

VIII.

Time and Genesis in Geography

THE GENERAL PROBLEM

One of the more perplexing problems in the field of geography is the question of the extent to which the study of any particular earth phenomenon, or of the complex of phenomena in inter-relation in space, must be carried back into the previous development from which it was produced. The logical problem involved is the same whether one is dealing with a man-made phenomenon, whose development reaches back in human history, or a land-form, whose development must be sought in geologic history. In either case the student who devotes the major part of his research to unravel past development may be challenged by some of his colleagues as working outside the field of geography; in the former case, he is accused of being an historian, in the latter, an historical geologist.

If we examine the substantive literature in geography since it became separated from history as an independent field of knowl-edge, there would seem little question that its primary purpose has been to comprehend the world as it is. As Hettner puts it, geography is a field for which "time in general steps into the back-ground" [*1*:184]. Cholley finds this viewpoint implicit in the very definition of geography [52:106–14]. Certainly it is implicit in the statement of geography as the study of the earth as our world.

Numerous critics have characterized this viewpoint as "static" in contrast to a "dynamic" view which they advocate. Any discussion on this basis is likely to produce more heat than light. To the best of my knowledge, no competent student of the methodology of geography has ever asserted a static concept or failed to recognize that the dimension of time is always involved [*1*:176–84]. It is necessary, however, to distinguish clearly the several ways in which time is of concern in the study of the geography of the present.

We must recognize, but need not consider as relevant to the issues under discussion, the inevitable lapse of time from the beginning of observation to final publication. This is significant simply as a source of error in our findings. Time is logically involved in at least four different ways.

1. Some extent of time must be included in what we call the present. We are concerned not merely with static earth features but with those in motion, whether air currents, streams, or the human activities of transport, which are the essential factors in integration among places. In studying the interrelations of productive phenomena in place, we must take a section of time long enough to cover at least an annual cycle, based on the round of the seasons; in view of the fluctuations of climate from year to year, we commonly require a longer period to establish "average" present conditions; in other forms of production, for example, in the steel industry, fluctuations from quite different causes likewise make it necessary to consider, as the present, periods of several years. The cross-section which geography cuts through the dimension of time must therefore have a certain thickness, or duration, to provide a representative picture of the existing situations. It is consistent with common usage to refer to such a period as "the present," although even the last immediate moment was in fact in the past.

2. Not only do many of the phenomena of the present vary through cycles and fluctuations, but they are subject also to cumulative changes. In commenting on a discussion of the relative importance in geography of *being* and *becoming* [*1*:183], Wooldridge reminds us that the two are not completely distinct [*92*:90].[1]

---

[1] While this statement is welcomed as a valuable correction, the statements in the original discussion do not seem to me to permit the summary that "geography would fix its whole attention on being rather than becoming" [*92*:89].

The full description of the geography of an area "as it is," even as considered for an infinitesimal moment of time, must include description of the direction and rapidity of change. To determine present trends requires examination of the course of change over a period of the past commonly longer than that required to measure the other characteristics of the present.

3. To the extent that the interrelations among phenomena are dependent on current processes, they can be analyzed in terms of the present. But in many cases the current processes do not explain why the phenomena occur in their present relationships; it is necessary to examine relationships established at some time in the past when at least some of the phenomena were quite different in character.

For example, we may explain the current operations of the steel industry at Bethlehem, Pennsylvania, in terms of receipts of coal from western Pennsylvania and West Virginia and receipts of iron ore from Lake Erie and the Atlantic ports of import. But in order to understand why there should be any steel industry in the Bethlehem district we must trace the development back to the time when the industry depended on nearby iron ore resources and on anthracite coal brought down the Lehigh Valley.

The conclusion that geography must use historical materials in order to explain the presence and character of existing features has been almost universally recognized since Ritter expounded the theme in his celebrated lecture on "The Historical Element in Geography" [22].[2] The so-called static theory, that geography could explain existing phenomena solely in terms of contemporary conditions, is an invention of the critics who attack it. In fighting this windmill they lose sight of the valid issues: the question of how far back in the past it is necessary or desirable to investigate the development of present features, and the degree to which geographic studies of the present should be organized in historical sequence.

4. A somewhat different issue is raised by studies which seek to explain, not the integration of phenomena, but the origin and

[2] It is asserted explicitly and repeatedly in the section on "History in Geography" in *The Nature of Geography* [1:179, 182, 183, 184], and has been demonstrated in my substantive works, which are listed as illustrations [1:19].

development of individual features in the present geography of an area. Such genetic studies, reaching indefinitely back in time, focus on the causes of development of particular kinds of features, and are considered by many as more closely related to the systematic sciences or to history than to geography.

In each of the preceding cases the past is used as an aid to an understanding of the present geography. The manner and degree to which time is important for this purpose varies notably in different parts of geography. Consideration in this study will be directed toward those topical fields in which major issues have arisen, namely in the geography of landforms and climates and, more generally, in cultural geography.

Geographers study the past not only as "the key to the present," but also in terms of its own geographic content. Each past period had its then present geography, and the comparative study of the different geographies through successive periods of time depicts the changing geography of an area. Thereby the historical dimension of time is combined with the dimensions of space. As in history in general, such studies need not start at any "beginning" period nor need they come up to the present. Studies of this kind will be considered separately under the heading of "Historical Geography."

TIME AND GENESIS IN THE STUDY OF LANDFORMS

The Geography of Landforms

Among all the phenomena of areal variation, the configuration of the solid surface of the earth is the most nearly static. This, of course, is far from true of the water surfaces of the lands, which we included in the previous chapter as part of the surface forms of the continents. This section is concerned with studies of the solid surface. Within whatever length of time we may include "the present," mountains, hills, valleys, and plains remain for the most part motionless and unchanging. As a statement of relative fact, rather than logical principle, this conclusion has its notable exceptions, as in the case of volcanoes, deltas, or meanders. In these, indeed, the idea of current change is implicit in the generic concept of the landform. In these cases the explanation of existing relationships may require an examination of past conditions. Richard Russell has shown that a study of the present geography of the Lower Mississippi Valley must take account of the important changes within recent historical time in river courses and flood plains—changes which have resulted in no small part from man's activities [from a lecture by Russell; cf. also *114*:9f.].

In the great majority of cases, however, the processes of change in landforms are so slow that little error results from assuming the landforms as static. What this means is that if we could go back in time far enough to analyze with a high degree of completeness the process relationships which have produced most of the other phenomena of area, we would find in most areas of the world that the character of the landforms and associated stream pattern was essentially the same then, and throughout the period of evolution of other phenomena, as we find it today. For however far back we can reach in time with any expectation of practical gain in studying the process relations of human phenomena, or even of natural vegetation, it is but a brief moment in the time-scale of evolution of most landforms. While we know in theory that there must have been some change in landforms during that brief moment, the error involved in ignoring such change is usually slight, perhaps no greater than the errors that are involved in an attempt to reconstruct the change.

The general principle developed in the preceding paragraph is recognized in Wooldridge's statement that the geographer studying the present "must limit himself to proximate, rather than ultimate genesis" [*92*:90].[3] Applying the principle more specifically, the geographer need study genesis only as far back as will enable him to attain greater comprehension of existing relationships of phenomena in areal variation; it is only the changes that have taken place during this limited period that are essential to his study. But if there have been essentially no changes in landforms within that period, "proximate genesis" is in effect reduced to zero.

For most purposes of geography, therefore, and for most but

[3] Wooldridge contrasts this statement with what he saw in a diagram in *The Nature of Geography*, which he describes as "instantaneous cross-sections" of geography with the phenomena of the systematic sciences. But the planes in that diagram are drawn with definite thickness, and the reader is warned that they "are not to be considered literally as plane surfaces" [*1*:147]; and a subsequent discussion refers to "a *limited* cross-section" of time, which "must be short enough so that *within* it . . ." [*1*:184, italics added].

by no means all areas of the world, geographers studying the relationships of landforms and stream patterns to the totality of phenomena may accept "the everlasting hills" as they are.

Genetic Geomorphology and Geography

To many geomorphologists it may seem a form of intellectual treason that geographers should ever think of limiting their view to a period which, however long in centuries, allows for no significant change in landforms. For the unique contribution to man's thought of the subject which for many decades was at the forefront of geography was the demonstration that the solid surface of our earth is but the temporary expression of endless change. It is common, however, in different branches of science to make use of concepts which are approximately valid for the purposes of that field, even though far from valid in other fields.

Each branch of science must be free to consider certain phenomena as they exist, as basic factors, even though in other sciences the same phenomena must be analyzed as products of complex structure or evolution. Otherwise every science would be required to duplicate the work of others. The geographer would have to study the planetary origin of the earth and the evolution of plant life before considering the relationships of vegetation to climate, landforms, and soil [*1*:307f.; similarly, Forde, *72*:228f.; Cholley, *52*:113f.; Le Lannou, *59*:37–45].

Discussions by geomorphologists of the value of genetic studies of landforms commonly reflect the historical development of their subject as serving the needs of two different fields. Geomorphology had its roots in both geography and geology, but its development in the nineteenth century was associated with the great rise in prestige of the natural sciences and with a more rapid development of geology than of geography [cf. Le Lannou, *58*: 273f.; *59*:42–45]. Consequently, regardless of where they were domiciled in the organized apartments of knowledge, geomorphologists tended to look for appreciation and a market for their intellectual products to geology rather than to geography.

If landforms are viewed as a particular category of phenomena, studies focused on processes of development lead to the construction of generic concepts and principles of deformation, of concern to systematic geology. When the development is studied as part of the total development of the earth's crust, for which the present is the key to the past, the study of landforms is an aid in establishing a chronological system, of concern to the student of historical geology. Such students as Ogilvie [*20*:75n.], Douglas Johnson, and Kirk Bryan [*100*:199] have all recognized that from this standpoint geomorphology is a working method within geology.

In contrast, Hettner asserted, if geomorphology is to serve the purposes of geography, "it must keep constantly in mind the causal interrelation (*ursächliche Zusammenhang*) with other geographic phenomena." This viewpoint tends to be neglected, he felt, when the emphasis is placed on determining the geologic age of surface forms, or on past features, such as peneplains, of which scarcely a trace remains in the present landscape [*12*:45].

Geomorphologists often fail to recognize this divergence of interest. Thus in an essay on "The Progress of Geomorphology" in the symposium on *Geography in the Twentieth Century*, Wooldridge states frankly that his "emphasis throughout has been on geomorphology as the complement of stratigraphical geology—a tool in the elucidation of earth-history," and as such "unmistakably part of geology." Nevertheless, "the methods and conclusions of geomorphology are necessary alike to the geologist . . . and to the geographer," and "the geographer cannot take landforms as given without intelligent scrutiny of their genesis." The analogy on which this categorical assertion is based considers landforms as objects in themselves rather than as the form of an object,[4] and further assumes that to say we must know structure is the same as to say we must know evolution [*3*:176f.].

A more common argument of those who insist that the geographer must follow the genetic approach in the study of landforms is that any alternative is dull and unimaginative, lacking in any "problem" worthy of intellectual efforts. Taken seriously, this would represent an argument either against geography as a whole or against the inclusion of any study of landforms within

---

[4] It is a common error to write of landforms as though they were actual objects. What is under study is simply the configuration of the surface of the earth, that is, certain limited aspects of a single object, the lithosphere.

geography. Rather, it represents a lack of imagination, or a form of myopia resulting from failure to recognize the purpose of the study of landforms in geography. The manner in which the form of the land is functionally related to other elements in the complex integration of areal variation presents a host of problems, the analysis of which requires intensive intellectual effort.

The observer standing on the suspension bridge over the Royal Gorge, looking a thousand feet down into the chasm, is presented with two different kinds of problems. On the one hand, what combination of mechanical forces with what differences in rock structure produced this extraordinary cut in the solid surface of the earth? On the other hand, what vision and planning of man constructed the even more extraordinary railroad through this gorge, what ingenious methods were developed to fasten it to the canyon wall and suspend it for a stretch over the cascading river? And what have been the far-reaching consequences in the development of productive areas behind the eastern rampart of the Rockies?

Areal variations in landforms are intimately related, in a host of cause-and-effect relationships, with areal variations in climate, soil, vegetation, agricultural practices, transport, and numerous political and strategic features. These interrelationships provide a host of problems, whose cause-and-effect relationships require investigation as essential elements in comprehending the totality of areal variation. Indeed, the difficulty here is not the lack of significant "problems," but rather their baffling complexity.

In many instances, no doubt, it may be sounder procedure to start with the conditions of agriculture or transport, seeking their relations to variations in landforms. But for the purpose of developing comparative studies of the significance of landforms there is also need for a study of the relationships in reverse—as in Ullman's study of the significance of the Columbia and Snake rivers in the regional geography of the Pacific Northwest [*120*], or the older studies in our literature of the importance of the Hudson-Mohawk depression or of the Appalachian barrier in general. But such studies require more than specialized knowledge of landforms, with a smattering of understanding of geography in general. To use the findings of empirical or descriptive geomorphology in studies of cause-and-effect relationships requires thorough knowledge of all the interrelated topical fields of geography.

A basic requisite for such studies is the development of ways of describing landforms in terms of characteristics that are most significant in relationships with other factors. To determine, in comprehensible and usable organization, that which exists in the confusing complexity of reality is a problem in itself, and the primary problem in the pursuit of knowledge. While landforms appear to be one of the most readily observable phenomena, they are at the same time one of the most extraordinarily complex. The configuration of the land is arranged in countless features, none sharply delimited from another, and all varying in size and in the three dimensions of shape. Further, these landform features vary in texture of surface materials and in structure of underground materials. Finally, the location of the diverse features in relation to each other, the areal distribution of different kinds of landforms, constitutes a complicated pattern of significance in geography. The task of analyzing these inherent characteristics as significant to man—the problem of generalizing the myriad variations judged to be minor in order to comprehend the significant landform character of an area—presents an intellectual problem of great difficulty.[5]

Students of genetic geomorphology are of course well aware of the baffling complexity of detail in the form of the land, and it is entirely understandable that they should believe that through the determination of genesis they have found the most effective way of measuring what characteristics are most significant. But "significant" by itself is a meaningless word. What is significant for one purpose may not be so for another, and each branch of science has different purposes. Coal is a material varying in content, structure, and location, and the significance of these vari-

[5] Edwin Hammond described some of the problems encountered in a research project on this topic in a paper read before the Association of American Geographers in 1954 (abstract in *Annals*, Vol. XLIV (1954), 210). A concrete example is offered by his student Robert N. Young, "A Geographic Classification of the Landforms of Puerto Rico," in *Symposium on the Geography of Puerto Rico* (University of Puerto Rico Press, 1955), pp. 27–46.

ations differs for the paleobotanist, the mining engineer, and the chemist; a study in paleobotany of how a particular coal deposit evolved will not necessarily tell the chemist what he needs to know about the coal, and contrariwise, the chemist can determine all that he needs to know about the coal without studying its evolution.

It is no answer to these specific arguments to assert as a universal law that "the best way of understanding anything is to understand how it has evolved or developed" [*93*:46]. Complete understanding of the evolution of anthracite coal would not in itself provide an understanding of what is required to start the coal burning. Even to the extent to which the statement has theoretical validity—that if we knew everything about the history of an object, we would have complete knowledge of the object in itself —it may be quite misleading in practice. The genetic geomorphologist cannot learn everything about the evolution of a landform and could not present all the details if he could learn them; but what he fails to learn, or omits as of minor importance in explaining the general course of its evolution, may be the particular details of most importance in current relationships with other elements of areal variation.

The test of any such theory is not in its logic but in its workability. Certainly there are cases—for example, volcanic peaks, basaltic dykes, or ridge-and-valley areas of folded rock—in which even partial knowledge of how the terrain was formed may aid the comprehension of its present character. In other cases, however, such incomplete knowledge may lead to quite erroneous impressions. In the case cited by Penck, the Bohemian massif is presented as similar to the Central Massif of France because of similarity in materials and general course of evolution [*1*:388f.]. In present landform, the two areas represent the fundamental contrast between concave and convex, but the development of this contrast in the most recent stages of evolution constitutes but a minor part of the total genesis in each area.

Whether explanatory analysis of development adds more than it detracts from a comprehension of the existing character of a landform as an integral element in areal variation is therefore a matter of judgment, rather than of logic. It is somewhat disconcerting that insistence on the value of such analyses for geography comes primarily from those who produce them rather than from those who use them.[6]

Genetic analysis may be expected to be useful in geography only to the extent to which it is designed to explain the existing form of the land in terms of those characteristics most signficant in interrelations with other elements of areal variation. To the extent that the geomorphologist is primarily concerned to use landforms as the means of studying geologic processes or determining stages in geologic history, his explanatory description, as Kesseli notes, is often "an explanation lacking a description" [107:5]. Russell, as well as Kesseli, concludes that a century of geomorphology dominated by the purpose of explaining genesis has failed to produce comprehensible representation of landforms for most areas of the world, including many that have been intensively studied by geomorphologists [114; 107].

The traditional concern of geomorphology to explain what has happened rather than to describe what exists is crystallized in the practice of classifying landforms in respect to genesis rather than to form. There is no necessary reason for presuming that a genetic classification will provide a useful classification of existing forms; experience has demonstrated that very often the reverse is true [1:388–91]. Ullman reports an additional example in a study of the significance of the Columbia and Snake rivers to areal variation in the Pacific Northwest. Such concepts as "antecedent," "superimposed," or "pirate capture" were found to be both unreliable and vague for descriptive purposes. More closely descriptive are such terms as "dioric" (a stream cutting through a mountain range) or "exotic" (a stream crossing a desert) [120].

These and similar protests which geographers have registered for more than a generation appear to run into a blank wall of

[6] The introductory and concluding comments to the study of *Structure, Surface and Drainage in South-East England*, which S. W. Wooldridge and David Linton published in 1939 (Institute of British Geographers, Publication #10), express views similar to those which Wooldridge has presented in subsequent methodological essays, together with the assertion that the study demonstrates the necessity of such genetic studies for the purposes of geography. Whether the examination of Mid-Tertiary folding and erosion aids the reader in comprehending the present configuration, and is the most efficacious method for that purpose, each reader must judge for himself.

dogma. Thus Peltier asserts without discussion that "a description . . . based on categories defined in terms of origin seems most likely to meet the requirements not only of geographers but also of the many others who have found applied geomorphology useful" [4:368]. Similarly, Wooldridge and East, when faced with an example of the failure of genetic description which they recognize as an "unanswerable argument," fall back upon an apparently universal principle that "the best classifications, including those of landforms, are genetic" [93:45].

Presumably this principle is derived from another, previously quoted, that "the best way of understanding anything is to understand how it has evolved or developed." This we found to be valid as a principle only if we have complete knowledge of the evolution, which is never possible. Moreover, a classification is by definition intentionally incomplete in many respects [101:85]. If the classification is based on genesis, it describes only those factors that have been most important in the course of development of the feature, ignoring factors of relatively minor or incidental importance in that history. But these may be the very factors that determine those characteristics which are of most importance in relation to other elements in the present geography.

One wonders whether the classification by evolution is not a carry-over from the biological sciences. While the determination of classification of biological specimens is based on their existing characteristics, the inclusion of different specimens in the same species constitutes an inductive theory that they are of common descent, hence in major part *identical* in genesis. If the theory is sound, one can anticipate far more similarity in present characteristics than we may have observed; that is, correct classification actually adds to our presumptive knowledge about the specimens.

This principle does not apply in the inorganic world. The inclusion of several entirely separate features in the same genetic classification is merely a reduction of the total explanation of each feature to the highest common factor. Whatever the degree of similarity, there is no presumption that other factors, and their consequences, will be similar. In short, no new knowledge is indicated.

Consequently, one may well challenge the presumption that

even for the purposes of dynamic geomorphology a genetic classification is suitable. In the normal procedure of science, classification follows immediately upon observation, in order that observable characteristics can be considered in generic terms. As the geomorphologists Russell and Kesseli both point out, the processes of
development of landforms can seldom be observed, but must be
induced from the study of observable characteristics [Russell in
conversation with me; Kesseli, *107*:5f.]. Classification by genesis is
therefore a classification of the results of scientific study, constantly subject to change not because of more complete or precise
knowledge of the observable facts but merely because of the development of new theories in the science.[7]

The Place of Genetic Geomorphology[8]

We have found that the same subject, the form of the land,
may be studied to produce contributions of knowledge both to
geology and to geography. For the purposes of geology, the present configuration of the land is merely a datum line, whereas for
geography, it is all important. The evolution of the landform, on
the other hand, is essential for the purposes of geology but only of
indirect concern for geography. Whether required, as in the case
of landforms of very recent change, or whether it is an aid in comprehending the present configuration, at most geography is concerned only with the development of the relatively recent past—
"proximate genesis."

The division of labor in science, however, cannot always fol-

---

[7] In checking for the *American College Dictionary* the meaning of terms taken
over by geography from common speech, I found that definitions given in
textbooks had changed through time as new theories of genesis developed.
On the assumption that the common folk who created these terms were concerned to describe simply what they saw, and that what they called an "estuary" should remain an "estuary" regardless of changing theories of genesis
and evolution, I defined such terms as estuary, fiord, cuesta, valley, mountain,
and delta by empirical description without presumption of genesis.

[8] The very brief discussion of this question in *The Nature of Geography*
stated explicitly that no attempt would be made to judge the proper answer
[*1*:423–25]. In spite of this deliberate fence-straddling, or because of it, several critics have inferred a viewpoint of opposition to the inclusion of geomorphology in geography. An inference which has been repeated several
times, though in clear opposition to the statement above, is based merely on
the fact that the word "landforms" appears on a diagram where the critic expected the word "geomorphology" [*1*:147].

low such logical distinctions. In this case, it appears to be determined rather by a specialized knowledge of materials and techniques. Individual geomorphologists have in fact carried out all three types of studies. Whether geomorphology is more logically associated with geography, with systematic geology, or with historical geology would appear therefore to depend on the point of view of the geomorphologist.[9] If that conclusion is sound, common sense as well as courtesy dictates that the decision in any particular case should be left to the geomorphologist.

The issue is not, as Hettner put it thirty years ago and Wooldridge more recently, whether a new generation of geographers will reject geomorphology [*12*:45; *92*:91], but whether geomorphologists have not lost contact with geography. Leighly's recent plea that students of physical geography should seek "simply to trace the operations of the laws of nature on the earth" sounds like a bugle call for the exodus [*108*]. On the basis of the discussion in the first section of the previous chapter, geomorphology should not expect in such an exodus to find itself part of a new coherent field of physical geography, but rather one of a number of disparate fields.

Conceivably, geomorphology might be surrendered to geology. In fact it is housed there in the division of subjects in many universities. Experience, however, demonstrates that geomorphology is of marginal interest to geology (this might be expected from theoretical considerations). Aside from its contributions to stratigraphy and chronology, its examination of the operations of natural laws on the earth adds repeated illustrations of geologic interest, provides information and "service courses" useful to students of other fields, but is not essential to the major problems in which most geologists are engaged. It is not surprising that there appears to be no urge among geomorphologists who have been closely associated with geography to migrate to geology, even when some geographers have been so unkind as to recommend such a move.

In geography, in contrast, thorough comprehension of the

[9] Wooldridge appears to have expressed essentially this conclusion, in 1945, if I understand correctly his comparison of the approach to geomorphology of W. M. Davis with that of Walther Penck [*92*:14].

characteristics of landforms is obviously essential in the study of variation, not merely in terms of generic types but also to provide understanding of the character of every area of the world. Geography, therefore, has every reason to welcome geomorphologists who wish to be at home in the same domain with them. Working together within that extensive domain, we are not permitted, under the principle of freedom of research, to impose rules or limitations on what studies any student may pursue. To expect a student of landforms—whether classified as a geologist or a geographer—to look upon a landscape without wishing to know how the present form of the land developed would be to deny him the fundamental spirit of science. To criticize a "geographic geomorphologist" because his pursuit of such knowledge carried him outside some presumed limit for geography would be impertinent.

If, however, geomorphology is to form an integral part of geography, it may be expected to accept its responsibilities to the over-all purpose of geography—the explanatory description of the variable character of the earth as the world of man. What Wooldridge calls "the seemingly endless and wearisome argument" among geographers over the place of geomorphology may be expected to continue as long as geomorphologists insist that the by-products of studies of landforms pursued for primarily nongeographic purposes are necessary and adequate for geographic purposes. If geomorphology is to fulfill its function as part of geography, it would appear appropriate for the geomorphologist to ask, rather than tell, other geographers what they need from geomorphology.

Differences in landforms constitute, obviously, one of the more significant variables in creating the total variation of areas. But this total variation consists not of the sum of features varying in area but of the integration of those features in interrelation. These interrelations depend on processes operating over a period of time during which various features are changing in form. To trace the development of landforms long before the processes of integration with other features commenced is not essential to an understanding of that integration. What is needed is the most comprehensive, measured, and usable description possible of the morphology of existing landforms, so classified as to permit generic studies of relationships with other earth features. The value to geography of studies in genetic geomorphology depends on the degree to which they are directed toward a fuller comprehension of the existing characteristics of landforms that are significant in functional relations with other earth features [similarly, Le Lannou, 59:42]. Thus geographers in general, whatever their individual specialties, welcome the proposals of Russell and Kesseli for "a more geographic geomorphology."

TIME AND GENESIS IN THE GEOGRAPHY OF CLIMATES

Major differences in the geography of climates, as compared with landforms, result from the fluidity of the atmospheric conditions. Within the span of time which we have called the present these change regularly and markedly through diurnal and annual cycles, irregularly through the continual changes of weather, and less markedly but often very significantly through variations from year to year. The length of time thus included in the present is also long enough to permit the determination of most of the causes of areal variations in climatic conditions—to explain why each area of the world has the kind of climate it has. Hence there is no major difference in time span, as in the case of geomorphology, between that needed for determination of the existing facts and that needed for explanation of their distribution.

When the interpretation of existing integrations leads back through a period of development, we commonly assume, even more than in the case of landforms, that climatic conditions have been essentially as they are today. As more reliable knowledge of climatic change is attained, this assumption may require major modification. But since the features most dependent on climatic conditions—vegetation and especially domestic crops—tend to change relatively rapidly with changes in climate, it should not be necessary in most cases to seek far into the past for an explanation of existing features.

For the history of geographic change, however, changes in climatic conditions through time may well be of major importance. Particularly in the areas of "marginal" climates, notably those of the subhumid-semiarid margin, we are greatly handicapped in interpreting past geographies, such as that of Mediterranean areas in classical times, until we have more reliable information on climatic changes.

The major issue among geographers today concerning the study of climates is the degree to which the geographer is concerned with the causes, or genesis, of climatic conditions. In climatology, as a science in itself, as one of the systematic sciences of the earth, the study of the processes and distribution of the phenomena of the atmosphere must necessarily include explanation of the reasons for differences in climates of different areas. The geography of climates, as an integral part of geography, is concerned to study the areal variation of climatic elements as integrated with other factors in determining limited or more complex integrations of areal variation. To what extent does the latter purpose require the former?

The comprehension of existing climatic conditions appears even less dependent on knowledge of causes than in the case of landforms. The measurements by which we describe and assess the characteristics of the atmosphere—level of temperature, amount of precipitation, percentage of humidity or cloudiness, velocity and direction of winds—can be used without knowledge of the causes producing them. This may well be the reason why such students as Hann and Ward considered the geography of climates as "essentially . . . descriptive in character" [4:345].

However, complete knowledge of the existing climatic conditions at any place involves far more than is supplied by, say, monthly averages. It may be urged that the student who is familiar with the causes of climatic conditions can use these, in combination with the data commonly published, to deduce additional knowledge. But such additional knowledge, as Brooks has suggested, can be more reliably secured from available raw data by use of a variety of computations more sophisticated than mere monthly averages [98:163–68].

On the other hand the network of climatic stations can never provide precise data for every locality. In areas where microclimatic differences are significant, knowledge of the relation of terrain factors to local variations in climate may be the only means available for determining climatic conditions at sites differing from those of the weather stations.

For most purposes in geography the problem is not the lack of climatic data but rather how to convert the great wealth of data available into statistical measurements which will be both comprehensible and at the same time effective in evaluating the aspects of climate that are significant in relation to other areal variations. Each of the several climatic elements fluctuate constantly through time, with significant consequences for many related features. Analytic description of the climate of any place requires the selection of computations which not merely reduce fluctuations to average conditions but also measure significant degrees of fluctuation.

The raw data of recorded weather observations offer an unlimited number of possible ways of computing significant ratios, such as those of thermal efficiency or of moisture surplus or deficiency, and of the fluctuations of such ratios through the period of "the present." A major problem in the geography of climates is to determine what computations will be most effective in assessing areal variations and temporal fluctuations that are most critical in relation to other earth features [cf. Brooks, *98*:163–68].

Both in construction and use, such computations are independent of the causes of climate. Rather, as Leighly emphasizes in a different connection, the problem is how best to relate the facts of climatology to the processes of the other geographic features concerned [*4*:355].

TIME AND GENESIS IN THE STUDY OF PRESENT CULTURAL FEATURES

Human affairs tend to fluctuate from year to year to a much greater degree than do natural phenomena. Hence it is generally necessary to consider a longer period of time as "the present." An even longer period is necessary to distinguish temporary fluctuations from changes representing definite trends.

In the study of past conditions to explain the interrelations of existing cultural features, the problems are considerably more complex than in the case of most natural features. A much greater number and variety of features are involved, all changing at different rates. While most of these change much more rapidly than do natural phenomena, their interrelationships may well have originated far back in time, at least in terms of human history [cf.

Le Lannou, *59*:41]. Hence, as we noted earlier, to explain the character of present features, we must repeatedly reach back into the geography of past periods [*1*:178f., 183]. "Each circumstance," Emrys Jones concludes, "must be set against the historical frame of reference wherein its origin lies, and it is in that context that the geographer will most nearly approach the solution of causes" [*74*:377].

Since all existing features originated sometime in the past, and some in the very remote past, are we not forced to study the present by retracing all past development? Undoubtedly, as Darby has observed, a complete interpretation of all that now exists would require going back to the establishment of the earliest relationship necessary to explain present features and considering the evolutionary changes since that time. But complete interpretation is never possible [*68*:9–11]. In a study of the present geography of an area we cannot follow every root to its deepest end; somewhere the scholar must cut off the diminishing returns [*1*: 358]. One cannot establish in theory where that limit should be; one can only say that in a well organized study there should be some rational balance in the depth to which the scholar pursues the varied phenomena and relationships back into the past.

While the answer to this question must depend on the judgment of the student in each individual case, the principle on which that judgment should be based is the distinction between expository description and explanatory description. The subject and scope of any study is defined by the former, however far beyond that the latter may lead. If we agree, as most students in practice have agreed, that what geography is primarily concerned to describe is the variable character of areas as formed by existing features in interrelationships, then explanatory description of features in the past must be kept subordinate to the primary purpose. Geography, Hettner concluded, "requires the genetic concept but it may not become history" [*2*:131f.]. The sense of Hettner's full discussion is perhaps even better expressed by a statement of Mackinder's: "Geography should be a description with causal relations in a dynamic rather than genetic sense" [*18*: 268].

Because French geography has developed in such a close relation with history, it is of particular interest to read Cholley's discussion of this problem [52:102–21]. Geography is concerned with areas, as they exist today, history with the differences in time. Yet invariably in studies in human geography, the young French student takes his course from history and seeks to reconstitute the entire chain of events that have led to the present situation. "Is this really necessary? The present is there, alive, active, and we can learn by directly observing the essential facts of its structure, appreciate its activity, measure its dynamism. It is by such observation that we can uncover that which goes back to the past . . . . Is it not sufficient to obtain from study of the past only that which is strictly indispensable to the comprehension of the present situation, to go back only to the epoch when we see produced the combination of elements which still constitutes the present situation without going back to the origin of each of the elements themselves?"

The latter would be impossible for the geographer, Cholley continues, and is unnecessary for his purpose. To understand a region of modern metallurgy, it is not necessary to follow the chronological facts since the origin of metallurgy, nor even since that of industrial work in the region under consideration; but it is enough to recognize the moment when the conditions of labor, capital, technology, characteristic of this modern form of exploitation, were found united. "It is, to be sure, a delicate judgment that has to be made and which is rendered easy if one bases it on consideration of the present geographic area he is concerned to explain. No matter how important a fact of human geography, it is no more necessary to reconstruct the entire history of its past than it is useful to retrace the entire geological evolution of a mountain like the Morvan. It suffices to show at what moment appeared the facts of present structure of the aspects which can account for the present morphology" [52:112–14].

If, as we have suggested, the primary purpose of geography imposes a practical limit on the extent to which existing cultural features are traced to their ultimate origins, it is obvious that there must be some place in the whole of the field of knowledge for studies concerned primarily with the genesis of cultural features which vary areally. Whether such genetic studies will be made primarily by students of the appropriate systematic sciences or by geographers will no doubt be determined on practical and personal grounds, which need not concern us here [1:373]. To the extent that they are useful for geography, such studies are to be welcomed, regardless of who makes them.

In view of the vast multiplicity of cultural features, however, it is important to remember that they are not all equally significant to the integration of phenomena in areas. Students who wish to avoid dissipating their efforts will select cultural features which are of major significance in the variation of areal integration, or which can be shown to be clear indicators of major factors which cannot readily be measured directly.

HISTORICAL GEOGRAPHY

While the purpose of most studies in geography is to describe and explain the world of the present, we noted early in this chapter that certain types of studies are focused primarily on the past. Geographers have always recognized a field of "historical geography," but there has been much debate as to what types of research are properly included under that title, as a part of the total field of geography.

There appears to be general agreement among geographers that studies seeking to explain history in terms of geography— which may appropriately be called "geographic history"—are logically a part of history, rather than of geography, even though geographers have contributed, and continue to contribute valuable studies [1:175f., xxv f.; similarly, Clark, 4:81f.].

Geographers also agree, I believe, that the geography of any past period, conceived as the geography of the *historical present,* to use Mackinder's phrase, is a form of geography essentially similar to what we commonly study, save for its dependence on historical records for its primary description [1:184–87, and xxxvi–xxxix; cf. similarly, Cholley, 52:77f.]. By adding to our storehouse of cases of particular categories of phenomena and interrelationships, as Clark has noted [4:96], such studies increase our ability to develop generic concepts and principles, notably in those fields, such as political geography, in which we may find at any one time in history only a small number of similar examples.

A special form of the geography of a past period as the historical present is the description of an area now inhabited at the time when man first entered it—that is, the natural geography of the area, or the depiction of its natural landscape. Except for those few areas for which we have descriptions by their first discoverers, such a study is not one of primary description but must be constructed from present observations and theories of process relationships. Much of our knowledge of "natural vegetation" of the well-developed areas of the world is of this type.

The geography of a single earlier period is "historical" only in the sense of dealing with the past, not in the sense of development. If, however, one studies a series of past geographies of the same area, the comparison of these successive cross-sections of time will reveal the results of the development that took place. The discussion of this subject in *The Nature of Geography,* derived largely from Hettner, provided no place in historical geography for studies focused directly on change through time [*1*: 187f.]. In the sense of "history" as the description of variation through time and of geography as variation through space, the two could not be combined—in this sense there would be no place for "historical geography." Subsequently Sauer [*115*] and Whittlesey [*126*] each presented strong arguments for a place for historical geography in the full sense of the study of the development of areas through time, and numerous other students have expressed similar views.

There are, I think, two major errors in the brief discussion leading to the conclusion stated in *The Nature of Geography.*

1. Although it is recognized that one can study the changes through time of any particular feature of an area, such a study is labeled as nongeographic, as part of the systematic study of that type of phenomena. This, however, is true only when the feature is studied only in itself. There is no reason why it may not be studied, in its changes through time, as a part of the character of the area as a whole, as the latter also changes through time. Darby subsequently demonstrated the validity of such a study in what he calls the "vertical theme" in historical geography: a particular category of phenomena, considered constantly as a part of the total geography of an area in interrelation with other areal

features, is traced in its evolution through time [*68*:8f.; cf. Monkhouse, *83*:22f.].

Similar work by Andrew Clark and his exposition of this theme in his chapter of *American Geography* [*4*:70–105] have been challenged by Cumberland on grounds similar to those stated in *The Nature of Geography:* "changes from time to time are the concern of history; differences from place to place are the concern of geography" [*94*:185]. But in this situation we have both: differences from place to place changing through time.

Here again, as in geomorphology, the test of geographic quality is in the purpose and focus of interest. If the concern is to determine the manner and processes of change, the study may be considered essentially historical in character; if focused on the changing character and relationships of a feature considered as part of the total geography of the area, its geographic character is clear.

2. The major part of the discussion of this topic in *The Nature of Geography* is concerned with historical studies of regions or of "landscapes" as wholes—a reflection of themes that were running strong in the current of geographic thought at the time. While logical objections were raised to the idea that a region would remain a "whole" through time, it was recognized that in theory one could conceive of a continuous historical geography of any area, formed by an unlimited number of past cross-sections in time. The sole objection stated was a practical one—it would be impossible to analyze such a motion picture [*1*:188].

If we imagine a series of air photographs taken of a single area in England, and from the same point in the air, on a mid-summer day every year during the past twenty centuries, and viewed as a motion picture film by geographers and historians, the historians would quite possibly consider it a historical picture, but certainly geographers would call it geographic. Each would see different things in the same picture. To the geographer, this would be a presentation of areal variation as it changed through time; if every individual photograph is geographic, surely the series as a whole is geographic.

Unquestionably, the problem of analyzing such a composite of variations through both space and time would be extremely complex. To emphasize the practical difficulty, however, cannot prove an impossibility; it is at most a warning that if any useful results are to be obtained, the ambitious student must seek ways of reducing some of the difficulties to the minimum. This can be done by selecting a relatively small region of restricted variation in area and affected by a limited number of factors producing historical change.

Other students have argued that it is unrealistic to think in terms of separate study of areal variations and temporal variations, that both should be integrated into one field—as much history as geography. Unquestionably, this would represent the study of the whole of reality, but it would abandon any form of specialization in method.

The attempts that have been made, whether by geographers or historians, at a scale involving continental areas and many centuries of time—or indeed on the world scale and for all human history—have proven more provocative of discussion than stimulating to further research [*1*:175f.; cf. also Spate, *87* and *88*]. If such integrated studies of history and geography are feasible at the research level, it would appear necessary to attain some measure of specialization by the selection of very limited sections of time and space.

While the purpose of historical geography, as the study of the changing character of areas through time, is not dependent on either our concern to interpret existing relationships within an area, nor on the concern for genesis, it may also contribute to both those purposes.

We concluded earlier that, in seeking the explanation of existing relationships of features, the normal procedure in geography is to start with the existing feature and trace back in time the processes of its relations with other features. But it is an error to assume that this procedure is sure to lead us to the past conditions which explain the present circumstances. For in all stages of the past the operation of any one process of relationship was necessarily modified by its total environment, an environment in which diverse elements were changing at different rates of change. The re-creation of the past, without restriction to those phenomena known to be related to present conditions, and the recording of relationships changing through time will enrich our knowledge of the kinds of relationships which we need to seek in the normal task of tracing present conditions through past processes to earlier circumstances [4:14].

From this point of view, however, studies in historical geography will be of most value in explaining present geography if there has been no marked discontinuity between the period with which they are concerned and the present. The geography of eastern North America at the time of discovery or first settlement is of value in understanding the present, but the processes of its development in previous centuries or millennia have relatively little carry-over to the present. Much the same seems true of Celtic and Roman settlements in England prior to the Anglo-Saxon invasions, in spite of a few striking exceptions. Similarly, the historical geography of a formerly rural area now completely covered by urban features may offer little to the understanding of the present city, other than of its street pattern.

Our consideration of historical geography has been limited to a world which has included man. This has been true in fact of nearly all studies written under that title. It might appear that logically there was also a place in geography for studies of the changing features of the earth in the eras before man arrived. To give significance to such studies we would have to change our concept of geography as the study of the world as the home of man, and speak, say, in terms of a "dinosaur geography." There are reasons independent of definitions, however, for this general acceptance of historical geography as limited to a past which includes man.

In the integration of phenomena which we are concerned to study in geography, man wherever he exists or has existed is a major factor, closely associated with the other variables of area. Even in the study of an uninhabited area, our concern is with its character in relation to human interests. The study of geography with man excluded even from consideration is a study of integration without its major integrating element.

In considering the earth as the home of man, our interest is not confined to present man but extends to the whole human race throughout its history. We are interested to study the different geographies of the past because those differences were due primarily to human beings thinking, planning, and working like ourselves. In terms of intellectual interest, the integrations which they established with other earth features are of the same order as those of present man.[10]

Finally, there is an important practical ground for limiting the geography of the past to the period of human history, in fact to limited portions of that period. Primary description of the geography of any past time is possible only if we have records of eyewitnesses. Lacking these, we are forced to reconstruct the geography largely by deduction from present conditions.

SUMMARY

The key to a proper understanding of the function of time in geography is the recognition that the constant concern of geography is to study phenomena not in themselves nor in their separate variations over the earth but in the areal variation of the phenomena as interrelated with each other, either in relatively simple integrations or in more complex but still partial integrations, in order to approach the total integration of interrelated phenomena which form the varying character of the earth as the home of man.

Some extent of time is necessary in the primary description of existing interrelationships and rates of change. Explanatory description of individual relationships may require analysis of process relationships considerably farther back in time, but the purpose of such dips into the past is not to trace developments or seek origins but to facilitate comprehension of the present.

Studies focused primarily on causal development or the genesis of particular categories of phenomena, including the reasons for their differential distribution over the earth, are logically a part of the systematic study of phenomena by categories—that is,

[10] The oft-quoted analogy which William Morris Davis first used to urge the study of the history of landforms represents unconscious recognition of a difference by personifying nature in order to deny the difference: "To look upon a landscape . . . without any recognition of the labor expended in producing it . . . is like visiting Rome in the ignorant belief that the Romans of today had no ancestors" [quoted in *92*:90f.]. The mechanical operations of natural forces, however, are not on the same level as the creative planning, organizing, and persistent exerting of mental and physical energy by man.

of the systematic sciences of nature or man. For practical and personal reasons, students specializing in particular topics of systematic geography will pursue such studies, but this imposes no obligation on other geographers to attain such competence.

While the areal variation of phenomena in integration can be examined directly only in the present, recorded descriptions of earlier observers provide us with materials which, combined with present observations of features known to have remained essentially unchanged, enable us to look at the geography of an earlier historical time as though it were the present. By studying a series of such views of the geography of an area, we may interpolate the record of changes in the character of an area. Such historical studies of changing integrations are essentially geography rather than history as long as the focus of attention is maintained on the character of areas, changing in consequence of certain processes, in contrast to the historical interest in the processes themselves.

IX.

Is Geography Divided Between "Systematic" and "Regional" Geography?

HISTORY OF THE PROBLEM

Whereas the "dualism" of a geography of nature and a geography of man was a peculiarity of the late nineteenth century, throughout the recorded history of the subject it has appeared to many students to be divided into two halves reflecting a contrast in method of study and presentation.

In the development of geography by early Greek and Roman students, there were those who considered its function was primarily that of organizing information about divers countries, while others sought to measure the earth, to trace rivers to their sources, or to establish climatic belts. Berger has described in detail the shifts in emphasis and controversies between opposing schools in Greek and Roman geography.[1]

In modern geography, most discussions can be traced back to the classic work of Bernard Varen (Varenius) of 1650. Using terms which one or more of his predecessors had used, Varen defined "general geography" as that part of the science (*scientia*) which "studies the Earth in general, describing its various divi-

---

[1] Vidal de la Blache, I find, also noted [26:130] the historical significance of the conflict between the two conceptions in the earliest development of the field, as described in passages scattered through a large volume by Ernest Hugo Berger, *Geschichte der wissenschaftlichen Erdkunde der Griechen*, Leipzig, 1883–92. The otherwise excellent histories of ancient geography published in English unfortunately give little consideration to methodology.

sions and the phenomena which affect it as a whole." It provides the "foundations" and "general laws" of geography which are to be applied in the studies of individual countries, which form "special geography." If geography as a whole was to "vindicate her claims to be called a Science," her students must pay far more attention than was commonly the case to work in "general geography" [62:56]. Consequently Varen, who in the previous year had published a regional study of Japan and Siam, of which most of the chapters dealt with human aspects, set himself the task of providing a systematic treatment of general geography, dealing largely, though not exclusively, with its nonhuman aspects. In the same work, however, he included a long outline of topics to be considered in a study in "special geography," and there is reason to believe that he intended to demonstrate this in later studies, but was prevented from doing so by his untimely death.

J. N. L. Baker has demonstrated, by careful study of the original Latin text (in contrast to later English editions found to be unreliable), that there is no reason for supposing that Varen regarded special geography as a less important part of the field than general geography, or that human aspects did not form an important part of his view of the field [62]. Vidal de la Blache, commenting on the same passages, concludes also that Varen's view of geography was not "dualistic": "The rapport between the general laws and the particular descriptions, which are their application, constitutes the intimate unity of geography" [26:134].

The contrast emphasized by Varen, both in his terms and in his explanation of them, is less the distinction between the approach by study of elements and that by study of areas, but more the contrast between generic and specific studies. Further confusion resulted when later students, notably Kant and Humboldt, substituted the word "physical" (from physics) for "general" and classified all generic studies, including those of man, as "physical geography." We need not here follow the course of the debates in Germany in the latter part of the nineteenth century, resulting in part from exaggeration by later students of the difference in emphasis between Humboldt and Ritter, and in part from the development of a more restricted concept of science [1: 70–96]. In consequence of those debates, and particularly of the programmatic position taken by Richthofen,[2] there was general agreement among German geographers at the turn of the century that the studies by elements and by areas were equally necessary and important in geography [cf. Hettner, *8*:8f.; *2*:398–403].

This balanced view, however, was shortly upset by new theories about regions as actual units of area which would permit the construction of generic concepts and presumably of general laws or principles, apparently independently of work in "systematic geography" [*1*: Chapter IX]. While the theory of regions as genuine entities, even as concrete objects or organisms, was short-lived, it left a residue of belief that one could construct generic concepts of regions in terms of total character. In Germany the multiple meaning of the word *Landschaft* facilitated the theoretical construction of a "systematic science of regions" (*Landschaften*) as the core of geography, relegating "systematic" or "general" geography to a lower level, if not outside the field entirely. In criticism of such theories, Schmitthenner and Lautensach have followed Hettner in demonstrating the essential importance of "general geography" [*44*; *45*:32f.; *37*:16–18].

In this country, on the other hand, many geographers appear to have reacted from overoptimistic theories about regional geography to question its place in science. Even in France, where geographers have been particularly acclaimed for their regional monographs, a number of students look to "general geography" as "the crown of geographic knowledge," the ultimate goal in geography. While challenging this viewpoint, Le Lannou recognizes that general geography is essential to the study of regional geography [*59*:134–57], a view which Cholley also expresses [*52*: 26, 57f.].

On the general assumption that, while history proves nothing, its weight of experience does provide lessons that are not to be tossed aside lightly, the developments in geography in the twen-

[2] In his Leipzig address of 1883 [*21*; *1*:91–93]. Because it was published only as an inaugural address, copies of this paper are unfortunately scarce. Though highly influential in Germany, it has apparently rarely been read in other countries. Mackinder does not name the paper in accepting Richthofen's conclusions [*17*:371], of which he may have learned secondhand from Wagner's biennial discussion of methodology in the *Geographisches Jahrbuch*. Gerland's critical discussion is not a reliable intermediary [*1*:116, footnote 44]. The original paper is available from the Library of Congress.

tieth century confirm the empirical conclusion that Hettner stated in 1898: that the long history of dispute and shifting emphasis from one side to the other in this controversy constitutes the strongest empirical argument in favor of continuous and interrelated advancement of both approaches in geography [9:306; 1:457].

On the other hand, the historical controversy has contributed to misunderstanding by presuming the existence of a dichotomy in geography. This has no doubt been encouraged by the terms we commonly use to describe methods of approach which differ far less than the terms suggest. Thus the term "regional geography" tends, as De Jong observes, to confirm the erroneous impression that the other kind of geography is not tied to areas [34: 60]. The terms "general geography" and "systematic geography" both tend to emphasize generic studies of particular phenomena rather than the study of phenomena in interrelation in specific places [2:399].

More particularly, the term "systematic geography" emphasizes an apparent similarity with the "systematic sciences," and thus encourages the view that one half of geography is composed of a series of branches each of which is a science in itself, studying a particular category of phenomena, each category defined in terms of the corresponding systematic science. It is as though the object of study in geography, the earth shell, was considered as formed of a series of more or less separate shells, each representing the category of phenomena included within a systematic science.

If systematic geography is considered as a series of studies each focused on the character, processes, and distribution over the world of individual elements, the work is logically similar to, and in many cases duplicates, that of the appropriate systematic sciences. It is not surprising therefore that repeatedly in the history of geographic thought it has been argued that systematic geography is not properly a part of geography [1:414–26].

Certainly many studies in systematic geography, notably in textbooks, include a large content that is concerned primarily with the structure, functions, and processes of particular phenomena, independent of place [2:133, 401]. If some attention is paid to the distribution of such phenomena over the earth, there is often little discussion of the interrelations with other areal variations.

No doubt this results in part from the fact that in order to analyze relationships among different earth features one needs to know certain of the processes of development of each of the features involved, processes that have been analyzed by the students of the respective systematic sciences. In addition, the fact that the related systematic sciences have in many cases established the principles of those processes with more certainty and more universal application than geographers have established principles of interrelation of different phenomena in different places increases their scientific standing. But if explanatory analysis is considered to be the mark of "science," such works are "scientific" chiefly in their nongeographic portions and largely descriptive in their geographic portions.

This is not to say that one can *separate* geography from the systematic sciences, but that their ultimate purposes of study differ. The distinction is more difficult to recognize between studies in systematic sciences which describe and explain the distribution of their phenomena and studies in geography which describe and explain the relations of such distribution to those of other elements as a part of the variation of areas.[3] This, however, is merely a reminder of the fact that all sciences are but parts of a single body of knowledge.

Other students have at times argued that "regional geography" must be pushed out of geography in the opposite direction. Since the analysis of the complex integration of heterogeneous phenomena of areas cannot be approached directly by the methods of the systematic sciences, and the areas cannot be treated as individual phenomena, regional studies do not belong in geography. Whether a form of applied geography or an art, they should not be included in a discipline striving to be a science.

In discussing this issue with certain French geographers who

---

[3] The distinction is expounded at length in *The Nature of Geography* on the basis of the writings of Richthofen, Hettner, Penck, Lehmann, Schmidt, and Michotte [*1*:92, 415, 426, 458], and has since been discussed particularly clearly by Cholley [*52*:57f.].

assert that "general geography alone is capable of taking its place as a science," Le Lannou takes the argument into his opponents' camp by attacking the assumption that any very large part of general (systematic) geography can hope to analyze its material in the manner and degree which they regard as "scientific" [59: 134–57]. Many students have supposed that the ability to carry out certain procedures of analysis possible in studying the elementary integrations of certain physical features was inherent in the nature of "general" or "systematic" geography, and that therefore the same should be true in all parts of that field. Such results, Le Lannou pointed out, have not been achieved in respect to the human aspects of geography, nor can they be expected in respect to all the "natural" aspects. Since most of the total integration of geography cannot be broken down into elementary integrations, the exclusion of regional geography as "unscientific" would soon need to be followed by the exclusion of most of what is now called systematic geography also.[4]

Whether geography can be considered a "science" or not is not a question that can be determined by amputating major segments of the subject as a field of knowledge. The complex integrations of phenomena varying through area constitute the reality of our world. To describe and, as far as possible, analyze and explain these varying integrations presents questions that undoubtedly are difficult to answer. But geography is the subject from which men have expected the answers and which has always sought to provide them.

THE LOGIC OF REGIONAL AND TOPICAL ANALYSIS IN GEOGRAPHY

To understand what is involved in this apparent dichotomy of methods in geography, we need to reconsider the nature of the geographic substance, the subject of study in geography. We have previously described the earth shell as filled with a multiplicity of heterogeneous phenomena varying over the earth, interrelated in

[4] The logical end of such considerations was indicated by a colleague in astronomy, who dismissed all "the so-called social sciences," and when asked concerning the biological sciences, expressed as his final conclusion (over cocktail glasses, to be sure) that only astronomy and physics were "true sciences."

place and interconnected between places. But the relationships and connections range in degree from very close to very slight. It is necessary now to consider the consequences of these differences in degree, both in respect to the integration of phenomena in place and to the integration of areas.

1. While many phenomena are interrelated in origin or development, others are largely or completely independent, though existing in immediate proximity. Some features in place represent integrations, as resultants, of phenomena in themselves largely independent—for example, wild vegetation in relation to climate, soil, land slope, and drainage, or farms in relation to factors of culture, economy, climate, and soils. Within the same small area which includes both farmland and woodland, there may also be mines, directly related to coal deposits, stream valleys, and railroads, but only in minor degree related to farms or woodlands; and there may be too a home for indigent old people, located here solely because of the successful efforts of a local politician. Thus the totality of phenomena at any place is not a single integration but rather a complex of loosely interrelated segments, each of which is formed of closely interrelated phenomena, together with some phenomena which show little or no relation with the others. Even if the latter are ignored, the complex of loosely related groups when studied in its variation through area shows different rates of variation for each of its component groups, and to a lesser extent for each of their constituent members.

2. While there is some degree of interconnection among all the places of the earth—for example, in atmospheric conditions—many phenomena at one place are largely independent of conditions at others, while some are closely connected. Not only are certain phenomena generally more dependent on areal connections, but there are great differences in the same phenomena in different parts of the world: some areas are more self-sufficient or more isolated, others more dependent on outside areas.

If the previous paragraphs present the general picture of the nature of the subject of study in geography, what do we wish to learn about it in detail? We noted early that the purpose of learning had two aspects: (1) human interest, or the need to know the facts about the world in which we live; and (2) intellectual concern to comprehend or explain the observed facts in their relationships. In geography, we noted, the former purpose is more widespread, immediate, and stronger than in many other fields, and the facts are more easily observed, whereas the relationships among them may be very difficult to determine. The first aspect, which may be served by superficial description, is an essential step preceding the second or scholarly purpose, and in itself serves an important human purpose even if the latter is not feasible.

If we can think of the geography of any one place, very loosely for the moment, as represented by a limited number of outstanding or "characteristic" features, then the geography of a larger area may be thought of as the variation of this geography of one place while the location is moved through the area, but again retaining only the outstanding or "characteristic" variations. Such knowledge the intelligent layman wishes or needs to know in greater or less detail concerning areas small or large, nearby or far away. Certainly he wants to know the world as a whole, in which he is an integral figure with potential relations to every part of it. Moreover, he wants to know the areal variation within his particular world realm, or continent, and its connections with the others. At successive levels of country, major region, district, or place, he is concerned to know with increasing detail the areal variation and connections with other areas, and may well be interested in a similar knowledge of the other areas as well.

Whatever the unit of area, the knowledge desired is only in terms of the areal variation within that area and its connections with other areas. The need cannot be supplied by references to studies of particular categories over a larger area, from which the reader could assemble whatever information applied to the area of immediate interest.

This concern for the individual character of areas, large or small, has its clearest expression in the universal fact that, long before the appearance of professional geographers, places known to man were given individual proper names, not as much later streets or houses were given numbers for the purposes of location, but as recognition of individuality.[5] The fundamental purpose of geography to satisfy this common human interest was most simply expressed by Vidal de la Blache in a statement which innumerable geographers since have echoed: "Geography is the study of places" [*1*:241].[6]

If the knowledge of areal variation, at any level of areas, is to go beyond a superficial description of outstanding characteristics, it is necessary to examine the many phenomena which in various combinations of closely or loosely integrated relationships and connections constitute the character of area at each place. The total combination of features may be divided for study into segments, each of somewhat closely interrelated features, and these subdivided into further segments, each including a lesser number of elements in closer integration, down to the single feature or element. But in each case the areal variation of the segment is studied in terms of the interrelations of its elements among themselves and with those of other areal features or elements.

This consideration of the anatomy of our subject suggests a comparison with human anatomy. In anatomy all the facts and relationships may be studied in terms of categories: bones, muscles, nerves, blood system, digestive system, etc. But anatomists also find it necessary to study and describe the anatomy of the head, arms, legs, feet, chest, abdomen, etc. Significantly, the two methods are described, according to an *Encyclopaedia Britannica* article, as "systematic" and "topographic."

In considering this analogy with geography, certain major differences stand out. In contrast to the thousands of bodies available for anatomists to study, geography has but one earth shell. The features studied in geography are much larger in number,

---

[5] Note that in certain cases mere numbers have in time acquired the character of proper names—e.g., Fifth Avenue.

[6] The phrase was written by Vidal de la Blache in 1913 [*27*:299]. It seems reasonable to presume that it was derived, directly or indirectly, from Ritter's famous phrase, *die irdisch erfüllten Räume der Erdoberfläche* [*1*:57]. Note also the statement of the Scottish philosopher, Alexander Bain, that the foundation of geography is "the conception of occupied space," *Education as a Science* (New York, 1879) , p. 272.

more difficult to classify in distinct categories, and in many cases their interrelationships are much more difficult to recognize. Also, the world is much less clearly articulated in area than is the human body in its "topographic" parts.

One result is that in geography it is very difficult to determine how best to break down the total complex of phenomena of place into categories for concentrated study. Because of the large number of elements involved and the varying degrees in which they are interrelated, regardless of similarity or dissimilarity in kind, it is useful to study their areal variation at different levels of complexity and in a variety of different combinations (see Chapter VII).

Furthermore, it is very difficult in geography to determine what areal breakdown will be most useful, but at the same time this procedure is more important than in anatomy because of the greater importance of proximity. In spite of the increasing amount of long-range movements which man has developed, it is still true that for most of the phenomena at any one place, including particularly man himself, connections and associations within a region extending a limited distance from that place are generally more important than those with more remote places [cf. Ullman, *123*]. It is, no doubt, a reflection of this fact that in practically every country in the world government is organized in terms of areal divisions.

It is not, however, necessary in geographic study that the breakdown by areas must be in terms of contiguity. In fact, we normally ignore this in the primary division most commonly used, by separating the lands from the seas. Undoubtedly we should often group the land areas by "cultural worlds," in order to reduce the extent of areal variation within each such group. For many purposes northwestern Europe, Anglo-America, Australia, and New Zealand form an appropriate areal group. For certain purposes, as in the study of agricultural geography, there may be value in grouping lands by major climatic belts, but this procedure leads to pitfalls if carried much farther. Only in special cases is the study of agricultural geography facilitated by considering as a group the lands of "Mediterranean climate."

Even if we were not concerned to examine individual areas

or particular complexes of phenomena, we must find some method or methods of analyzing, whether for purposes of description or explanation, the extraordinarily complex subject of our study—the earth shell.

We may diagram our problem by stating more completely the theoretical illustration used earlier. Let us consider g, the totality of areally variable and interrelated phenomena at any one small location, x, together with all the interconnections of x with other places, as constituting the complete geography of x. Then the geography of the world would be represented by all the variations of g, as the location of x varied over the entire world. It would, of course, be impossible to attain such completeness of knowledge about any place, x, and, if we redefine g to represent the most we could learn about any place, x, it would be impossible to learn g for *every* location of x over the world. Such completeness indeed would be highly undesirable, since it would overwhelm our libraries with details of minute or inconsequential items.

Consequently, we not only accept (with some relief) the limitation of the possible, but we need also consciously to exclude whatever is of minimum significance, even though we are able to observe it. Thus, as noted in an earlier chapter, we ignore phenomena of g which appear to have but slight relation with other phenomena, whether at the place x or any other. Likewise we ignore minor noncumulative variations of g, as x shifts from place to place. We may even dismiss major variations of g at exceptional places within an area in which g otherwise varies little. By these means we may state with a high approximation of truth that as x varies through certain stretches of area there is no significant change in g.

If then we have changed the concept of g to represent the maximum knowledge desirable concerning the place x, we still have a highly complex variable to study. For while certain of its elements may vary, from x' to x'', at much the same rates, other groups of its elements, or individual elements, vary in area at different rates. Our problem is still far too complex to handle in terms both of g, though reduced as above, and of areal variation over the earth, reduced as above. We must break down into smaller portions either *g* or the world, or both.

To the extent that we divide *g*—the maximum knowledge desired about a place *x*—into more closely integrated segments at successively less complex levels, we can study the areal variation of each segment over the world in increasing degree of precision. The closeness of the integration, it should be noted, does not depend on similarity in intrinsic qualities of the phenomena included. The classification of elements into inorganic, organic, and human provides no criteria of closeness of integration. Areal variations in vegetation may be closely integrated with climate, and coal deposits are significantly integrated in geography only with human activities, in coal mines. In determining what phenomena to include in separate segments, therefore, we select those which show the most marked correspondence in areal variations, suggesting the existence of close interrelationships among themselves or of dependence on a common controlling factor.

When we divide area, the world, into sections, the less the areal variation within each section, the more completely can we analyze the variations and relationships involved in the variable *g*. In this case it is obvious that the degree of complexity of areal variation in each areal section is only in part dependent on size; in some areas, even though divided into quite small sections, there may still be a large degree of areal variation.

Either method, it must be remembered, violates the unity of the geography of the world, for the several segments or individual elements of *g*, the geography of a place, are in fact interrelated in some degree with each other, and the various sections of the world are interconnected in many ways. Consequently, if *g* has been broken down into segments, it is necessary in studying each segment to take into consideration the relations of its phenomena with those of other segments; if the area has been broken down into regions, the study of each region must take account of its connections with others.

If we are concerned to study areal variations simultaneously throughout the entire world, it is necessary to restrict the phenomena to a very small segment of the total, commonly to a single element or an element-complex of such close internal inter-relationship as to form essentially a unit. This method offers the great advantage of concentrating on the areal variation of one variable in relation to others. By this means one may observe patterns of covariance of area suggesting hypotheses of causal connection, which may be demonstrated by studies of process relationships. This "systematic approach," therefore, permits the development of generic concepts and general principles or laws.

Unfortunately, however, this method of isolating single elements or element-complexes for study *over the entire world* has only limited possibilities. It is most useful in the case of the oceans, climate, landforms, or natural vegetation. To the extent that the phenomena are dependent on man, the very great differences in culture, technology, economic levels and institutions in the different parts of the world will dominate the areal variation of the phenomena studied. Thus the only clear positive conclusion to be drawn from a study of world rice production is that rice is grown, if at all possible, wherever the cultural heritage includes the use of rice in the daily diet. For other significant conclusions about the geography of rice, it is necessary to study separately those parts of the world where the cultural heritage includes rice consumption and those where it does not. If, conversely, we include the human factors in the segment of phenomena whose areal variation is to be studied, that segment becomes excessively complex for a world study.

This conclusion may explain a situation which many students have commented upon. After more than fifty years since Ratzel first attempted to organize the human aspects of geography systematically, we have few world studies of the predominantly human features comparable to those of climates or landforms. The same difficulty is clearly present in world studies of such features as soils and mineral resources. As an exception which tests the rule we may note the case of petroleum; thanks to interconnections of areas and the special importance of that mineral, its discovery brings to it a common economic culture and technology.

In practice we have long recognized the principle involved in restricting both the segment of phenomena to be studied and the area of study. If the area studied is restricted to a single country of more or less approximately universal culture, technology, and economic level, there is a much greater possibility of establishing generic concepts and principles concerning features of predominantly human origin; but these concepts and principles cannot be assumed to be applicable outside that country.

The greater the complexity of phenomena included in the single segment whose areal variation is under study, the more narrowly must we restrict, by subdivision into smaller, more nearly homogeneous units, the area of variation. The complete complex of geography could be studied only at a point.

Consequently, we conclude from theory what is obvious in our practice, that we cannot study the complete composite of significant phenomena of geography for a single area; we can present that of each of the segments, but since these vary somewhat independently within the same area, however small it may be, we cannot integrate the total complex.

In sum, geography cannot be considered as divided between studies which analyze individual elements over the world and those which analyze complete complexes of elements by areas. The former are logically a part of the appropriate systematic sciences, the latter simply cannot be carried out. All studies in geography analyze the areal variations and connections of phenomena in integration. There is no dichotomy or dualism, but rather a gradational range along a continuum from those which analyze the most elementary complexes in areal variation over the world to those which analyze the most complex integrations in areal variation within small areas.[7] The former we may appropriately call "topical" studies,[8] the latter "regional" studies, pro-

---

[7] Bobek recognizes studies at the most feasible level of integration as regional geography (*Länderkunde*), and proposes that all at the intermediate level be recognized as a third class [*30*:139]. In terms of the present problem, it seems to me more important to recognize that there are an unlimited number of intervening steps.

[8] It is true that if we trace back the etymology of "topic" we arrive at the same root source as that for the word "topography," but fortunately we are accustomed to use the word "topic" in English without any connotation stemming from its origin. This is a case in which it is evidently preferable to ignore genesis!

I

vided we remember that every truly geographic study involves the use of both the topical and the regional approach.[9]

INTERPLAY OF THE TOPICAL AND REGIONAL METHODS

We concluded earlier that most studies in geography require the use of both topical analysis and area analysis. The segment of phenomena under study is broken down into less complex groups of more closely integrated elements, and the area is broken down into smaller, less heterogeneous or less interconnected parts. In a well-organized study, the two procedures are carried out in relation to each other—whether the student is conscious of the process or not.

Let us suppose that the student decides that in view of the complexity of the phenomena involved he will first break down the total area of study—say, a continent—into lesser parts permitting easier analysis of the total complex. A first step may well be to determine which of the elements cause major variations in the total complex among different parts of the continent but only minor variations within each part if the continent is divided on that basis. By using this division as his first step he has reduced the number of variables to be studied within each areal part. He may then proceed, within each areal part, to determine in similar fashion how it may best be subdivided in order to reduce still further the complexity of phenomena that vary within each subdivision.

Contrary to traditional practice, there is no reason to assume that we can arrange the elements involved in a standard order of importance. This will depend both on the particular segment of reality under study—differing for agricultural geography and for manufacturing geography—and on the particular continent under study, and likewise, at lower levels of division, for each part under study.

[9] The viewpoint presented in this section, which differs markedly from that presented in *The Nature of Geography*, reflects ideas received from more sources than I am able to identify. Hettner had suggested that there was a series of gradations between general and regional geography [2:399]; Ackerman's study of 1945 vigorously attacked the concept of dualism between the two [95]; in the course of revising the present discussion, I was aided particularly by questions raised by the editor, and by Bobek's study [30], which only then came to my attention.

The process we have been describing necessarily involves preliminary analysis of the complex of phenomena under study to determine how it can best be broken down into simpler and more closely integrated segments or individual elements. This may appear to pose no special problem, because we are accustomed to start with "natural features" which appear to fall easily into a relatively small number of categories. We forget that the interrelationships of phenomena which determine their integration do not depend on categories but on the characteristics of individual elements. Climate may be a misleading summary expression for moisture, temperature, and winds; water is not the same geographic element in surface waters, in soil, in rock structure, in ice, or in water vapor. Certainly, the phenomena of human origin may be extremely difficult to classify into functionally significant types, as anyone who has worked with census data or in mapping urban structures can testify.

If we were forced to study every element individually, our task would be so vast as to appear hopeless. We take a major step forward if we can establish the existence, as a generic form, of an element-complex, an elementary integration of two or more dissimilar elements closely dependent on each other [1:428–31]. Well-known examples would include such obvious cases as steep slopes of thin immature soils; flood plains as nearly flat areas of fine soil but inadequate drainage with water available for irrigation; taiga areas dominated by narrow-leaved evergreen forests, podzol soils and subarctic climate; terraced vineyards on steep, sunny and coarse-grained, well-drained soil; crop-animal complexes in farming; iron and steel plants as complexes of blast furnaces, steel furnaces, rolling mills, warehouses, railroad sidings, etc.; copper-ore deposits, mine works, and smelter with other associated features (including residential).

This variety of examples has been cited in order to indicate that the first level of element-complexes may be formed from the integration of factors from the widest range of categories, inorganic, organic, and social. Because recent work in the construction of element-complexes by German geographers assumes a system of building up by steps through these three categories [cf. Bobek, *30*:126–30], we must look more closely at this question.

In doing so, it is necessary to distinguish an element-complex, as an association of elements whose areal variations are closely integrated, from the sum of elements only slightly interrelated in their areal variations. In combining particular grades of temperature and rainfall in one "climatic type," as in the systems of Koeppen and Thornthwaite, we produce a "multiple-feature type" which is no more than the simultaneous descriptive generalization of two largely independent elements. For cool regions may be dry as well as wet, and so too may hot regions.[10]

While the inorganic elements form certain element-complexes which are well known, for the most part they exist in proximity to one another without interrelation. This is clearly the case in the macroscopic view of the world: rugged terrain may be hot or cold, wet or dry and sandy soils are found in all types of climates and all types of landforms. Soil, to be sure, is in part the product of conditions of slope, bedrock, rainfall, and temperature, but soil is an essentially meaningless concept until we include vegetation as the integrating factor. More broadly, we may generalize both from empirical observation and from our knowledge of processes that it is primarily through organic forces that the heterogeneous inorganic materials of the earth shell have been integrated into element-complexes.

Passarge and his followers emphasized vegetation as the key indicator of the integration of "natural geography" [*1*:300–305, 315–20]. But while natural vegetation is closely related with variations in elements, of climate, soil, and drainage, it is relatively indifferent to very considerable variations in landforms and, of course, bears no relation to minerals below the level of the subsoil.

The element-complexes formed by vegetation have been destroyed or altered over much of the world by what man has

[10] The fact that Thornthwaite's indices of thermal and moisture efficiency are computed in part from the same data may give the impression that the two indices form together an integrated element-complex. The index of thermal efficiency is such an integrated element-complex, but as "evapo-transpiration" it is but one factor in the index of moisture efficiency, essentially independent of the other major factor, precipitation. In simple terms, there is, unfortunately, no functional relation on earth between the need for rain and the facts of rain. Thornthwaite's own discussion is quite clear on this point [*118*:65].

done to the natural vegetation. As re-created by the geographer, they are products of theory rather than reality. In their place, however, man has created a far greater variety of element-complexes, at elementary as well as at higher and more complicated levels. Many of these include very close integrations of inorganic and organic elements as well as social ones. Thus, in the mapping of "natural" complexes of inorganic elements for the *Naturräume* of Germany, the integration is determined by "usefulness" (*Nutzbarkeit*). But even if we can assume culture to be constant for the area of Germany, this measure certainly will vary in relation to urban markets.

The element-complexes which man creates with inorganic and organic elements may be independent of those established before man. Thus in Northern Interior United States the element-complex represented by the "Corn Belt" farm, an integration of type of landholding, fields, barns, machine cultivation, and a particular crop and livestock combination, extends with relatively minor differences over former forest or grassland, but in close relation with other conditions of soil, relief, and climate. Man also has established element-complexes directly with inorganic earth features without the use of organic features, as in the close and, in one direction, absolute integration of mines and mineral deposits.

It is true, as Bobek points out [*30*:129f.], that the element-complexes formed exclusively by inorganic elements are more stable than those which include organic elements, and that the latter are—or rather were—more stable than those in which man is an element. It is also true that the analysis of process relations in the first case involves only the laws of physical science, in the second case the somewhat different laws of biological science, while in the third case we are forced to deal with the greater uncertainty of generalizations concerning man and society. But since we must deal with the latter sooner or later in studying any total complex in which man is involved, it is not clear that any gain results from attempting to break down the actual integrations we observe in order to analyze less real integrations. What is ignored here is the fact that man, no less than flowing water or wind, is an agent of physical force producing physical effects.

Through the last few thousand years man, operating in social groups, and by harnessing first a few animals and later mechanical power, has been the greatest physical force creating element-complexes over large parts of the world.

There are, however, certain important limitations on the use of element-complexes of human origin. One results from the individuality of men: the individual farmer, for example, may choose to combine the same elements in a combination different from his neighbors. Whether this reflects freedom of the will or some trauma in his infancy is beyond our powers of investigation. But when we assume that the plurality of farmers can be considered as a single control, this is true only to the degree that all are operating under a common social-economic system. Consequently, we must expect a different set of element-complexes in each major culture area [cf. De Jong, *34*:69f.].

We conclude, therefore, that in analyzing the complex composite of phenomena to be studied in its areal variation, we seek first to determine what are the element-complexes which can, and should, be studied in areal variation as integrated units, regardless of the nature of their individual elements. The test of the validity of the complex as an integration is to observe whether its elements in variation through area demonstrate a close interrelationship.

If we find that many of the elements are included in several such closely integrated element-complexes, the next step is to determine what relationships exist among the complexes and the degree to which these can be combined in a complex, though necessarily looser, integration of a higher order—for example, farming and associated trading activities. As each higher step of looser integration, the different parts of the complex vary with increasing independence of each other, and the areal divisions must be subdivided so that covariance will be limited to ever decreasing area.

The procedure described in theory in the previous paragraphs necessitates a repeated alternation of study between the topical and areal methods of analysis, with repeated testing of hypotheses through trial and error to determine the most effective organization in both analyses. The question therefore arises whether it would not somehow be possible to organize our studies by either method alone.

Since the geographic study of any element or element-complex includes the study of the relationships of its variations to those of others, Ackerman suggested some years ago, and Wilcock has recently repeated the challenge, that "if the systematic studies are perfect, they could be added together to form regional geography" [95:138; 91].

We must agree that a summation of complete and perfect topical studies of a large area would include all the facts and relationships involved in the regional study of its geography. But the relationships involved in each part of the area would have been presented in scattered pieces throughout the different chapters. There would still remain the problem, not to be solved by simple addition, of gaining knowledge and understanding of the over-all integration as it varies in different parts of the area. It is true that the regional breakdown, since it cannot reach the ultimate of describing every place within the area, will not provide a complete picture of the areal variations of this over-all integration. But it does provide a series of descriptions of the character of that resultant, each of which gives a generalized picture of the actual situation within the region it purports to describe, a region within which the over-all integration varies less than it does over the entire area.

Further, to the extent to which the regional breakdown is sufficiently detailed so that the individual descriptions of the totality of phenomena for each region approximate the actual conditions of variation within the region, the mosaic presented by these regions on the map provides an approximation of the total structure of the area. It constitutes, in short, an integration, rather than a mere composite, of the structural patterns presented by separate topical studies. Similarly, we use this mosaic as the basis for considering the composite of interconnections which, as spatial interactions of elements or element-complexes, are studied separately and more accurately by the topical approach [1:439–41; 34:83ff.]. Because the results are far less accurate than those attained by topical studies, the approximate view of the total structure and function of the area thus attained has far less value for further research, but represents an end-product providing us with the maximum comprehension of the reality of places.

In contrast, there were many students a few decades ago who believed it should be possible to analyze the substance of geography by direct examination of areas, classifying them in a system of orders and types. Most writers on this question appear to have accepted, or arrived independently at, the negative conclusion reached in *The Nature of Geography* [*1*:311–65, 439–44]. In Germany, Obst recently reasserted this view, to which Schmitthenner replied in effective amplification of the earlier critiques of Hettner [*44; 45*:32f.]. Lautensach also has re-examined the problem, in an essay based on wide study of the literature, and concludes, in agreement with *The Nature of Geography*, that "areas cannot be classified logically according to their total character" [*37*:16–18].[11]

In this country, Van Cleef has urged that we apply Ritter's method of regional study, but in terms of areas far more minute than even those now called "microgeographic": "geographers must observe every square inch of the earth's landscapes hoping to find enough repetitive cases to enable him [*sic*] to convert hypothesis into law" [*124; 125*]. It requires little computation to demonstrate that his admission that the proposal "seems" impractical is an understatement. Rather one should ask what reason there is to hope for repetitive cases.

Our previous examination of the nature of the complex integration in any area provides the answer. In any part of the world in which man is included, we can be sure before we start the search that we will not find the same integration repeated in areas of different culture, or in areas of different climate, and these two factors vary over the world largely independently of each other. Further, when we consider the significance to the integration existing in any area of its connections with other areas, we must recognize the unique character of each area of the

---

[11] Lautensach further offers a positive proposal, which he has developed over the past twenty years, under the term *"Geographische Formenwandel"*: the study of change and rate of change (in relation to area, not to time) of the character or form of geographic features individually and collectively [*37*:20 ff.; *38*]. The concept, which merits more attention than can be given here, has been discussed at length by Schmitthenner [*45a*].

world, since there can be no repetition of the location of an area in respect to the other areas of the world.

The great majority of geographers have recognized that the world does not consist of a mosaic of distinct regions, and that we cannot hope to classify the more complex integrations of areal phenomena in a single objective system of regions. Nevertheless, they recognize that in order to analyze complex integrations in terms of a limited range of areal variations it is necessary to divide large areas into smaller parts. The purpose in dividing the area is to secure areal sections, or "regions," such that within each region the elements of the segment of integration under study will demonstrate nearly constant interrelations and the maximum degree of interconnections among places, while discontinuity in both respects shall occur primarily along the lines of division among the several regions. The more complex the segment of integration under study, the greater must be the degree of areal division. The "regional concept" and the "regional method" must therefore not be confused with what we commonly call "regional geography," as Preston James has pointed out [4:9]. The regional concept is applicable, and the regional method is used in fact at every level of geographic study, along the continuum from that of the study of the most elementary integrations (the extreme topical approach) to that of maximum integration (the extreme regional approach).

The confusion to which James refers results, no doubt, from the fact that we use the word "region" for a number of different concepts, each of which bears a different relation to the contrast between the topical and the regional approach. Analysis of these different concepts and their uses in geography will serve to demonstrate further the gradational character of the differences which erroneously we have tended to consider as a dichotomy.

In its historical development, the concept of a region in geography developed from the need to divide a larger area into parts, each to be studied in terms of maximum integration. In such a division, as Hettner pointed out as early as 1903, it was necessary to consider not only all significant similarities in the character of places, but also the location-relationships of reciprocal connections among places [*10*:197; repeated in *2*:280f.]. Since these two sets of conditions are in large degree independent of each other, or indeed may be related in opposing patterns, they cannot be combined on a logical objective basis. Regional divisions made by different students, and the regions set up by the same student, show marked differences in the relative importance assigned to homogeneity of character as compared with degree of interconnection. In addition, the problem of scale presents a dilemma. One of the outstanding characteristics of the earth surface is that in some areas variations are minor and gradual, in others very marked and irregular. Likewise, in some parts of the world there is an intimate interconnection among places over wide areas, in others only over very small areas. Hence the construction of a usable regional division, avoiding an excessive number of unit-areas varying greatly in size, forces the student to make a variety of subjective compromises with reality. Commonly one is forced to accept certain areas as units even though each is notably heterogeneous in character and lacking in close interconnection, but is distinguished only by the fact that each of its parts is different from adjacent regions and all parts share approximately the same location.

If we seek to determine the meaning of the term "region" as used by geographers in studies of the type commonly called "regional," we must in most cases ignore any introductory definition and consider empirically the nature of the areas they call by that term. On this basis, the most that can be said is that *a "region" is an area of specific location which is in some way distinctive from other areas and which extends as far as that distinction extends*. The nature of the distinction is determined by the student using the term; if not explicitly stated, it must be judged from the context.

Such usage of one of the most important terms in our professional language may appear very loose, particularly in comparison with the efforts of many geographers to formulate precisely a technical definition for a region. On the other hand, this loose meaning is entirely consistent with popular usage.

Standard dictionaries define the word to mean simply a more or less extensive area of indefinite but continuous extent. But in using the special word "region" rather than simply "area" or "piece of area," even the layman implies that he regards the area called by that word as standing out in his mind, as being in some way distinct. This is illustrated in such common uses as "the forest region of Wisconsin," "the Chicago region," "the region of southeastern Colorado," or simply "our region." In each case the different parts of the area called a region are assumed to have in common some characteristic or association, including as a minimum a common location. In its most widespread use in geography, the term is employed, therefore, in essentially the same sense as in common usage.[12]

Recognizing the vagueness of this concept of "region" as generally used, geographers for many years, as Whittlesey observed, "have been trying to shape and sharpen the technical meaning of the term 'region' into an instrument more powerful than the non-technical usage provides" [4:21]. But any attempt to define the concept in terms of all significant aspects of areal variation was defeated by the lack of covariance among significant features. A realistic division into regions, no matter what the definition of region, forced the student to make subjective decisions in weighing the importance of different phenomena. In order to fashion the concept of region into a sharp technical tool that could be applied objectively, it was necessary to abstract particular areal characteristics from the total reality, that is, to consider only individual features or elementary integrations of closely related features. This necessarily separated the two main types of areal relationships which, as Hettner noted, are involved together in a realistic regional system, namely, those of likeness and difference in phenomena in places and those of interconnections of phenomena among places.

Until quite recently major attention was focused on the concept of regions as areas of homogeneity—that is, of approximate uniformity of character. Under this broad category geographers

[12] Similarly, Hans Carol concludes that the German term *Landschaft* is in fact used to describe *"einen beliebig begrenzbaren Ausschnitt der Geosphäre"* [*31*:248; *32*:114], a view, however, which few other German geographers accept.

have found useful a great variety of somewhat similar but distinct concepts. In general, homogeneous regions differ in concept in at least three logical respects: (1) whether determined on the basis of one or more independent elements or in terms of demonstrated integrations of two or more elements; (2) whether considered in unique terms for each specific region or by generic criteria which may be applicable to any number of similar regions [*1*:293]; and (3) whether part of a system dividing the entire area under study, or the world, into discrete parts, or one which takes account only of certain parts of the area, omitting other parts.

In the common systems of "climatic regions," or "soil regions," or in large degree also of "agricultural regions" or "manufacturing regions," no integration of elements is involved. These are merely descriptive generalizations of quantitative measure of one or more elements varying independently over area. Since the number of possible combinations increases geometrically with the addition of each independent variable, it is hardly possible to combine a series of classes of more than two factors without producing an inordinate number of regions. If the independent factors vary in relative importance, as is generally the case, any apparently logical hierarchy of regions and subregions will be in conflict with reality [*1*:320–24].

Since no areal interrelations are involved, a division of the world into regions of this kind is no more than a classification of places, each place considered independently of others. It is a classification table put on a map, which enables us, by interpolation, to describe approximately the character of certain features of a large number of places simultaneously. The concept is therefore a generic concept about places, rather than a concept of specific pieces of area. To be sure, when all the places have been classified and the classifications marked on a map, there appears a pattern of distinctive areas; but the extent and shape of each area depends on the limiting criteria chosen by the student.

Regardless of the degree of precision of the criteria and of the objectivity of the determination of areal limits, such a system is logically merely a form of description reflecting subjective, or even quite arbitrary, determination of what degrees of variation are important. It has therefore been suggested that the areal divisions resulting from such a system should not be called "regions" but simply "areas of a certain type" [*1*:312, 392; *34*:69ff.].

The term "areas of a certain type," however, is also misleading in suggesting that all the places within any one area are in some way "typical," and hence that the area is notably homogeneous. Actually, all that has been determined is that the range of variation of the critical phenomenon within the region falls within a certain division of the total range of variation of that phenomenon over the earth. It does not follow that each part of the region is more like the other parts of that region than it is like parts of other regions. For example, if one should divide eastern North America by drawing any set of east-west lines across it, each of the resultant parts can be called a climatic region, no less homogeneous than those established by any standard set of divisions, such as that of Koeppen or Thornthwaite.

Any system of regions based on classification of one or more independent features is a generalized form of presentation of distribution, and bears the same relation to geography as any other form of presentation of the facts of distribution. One may consider it as a first step in systematic (topical) geography or as a necessary preliminary, more logically a part of the appropriate systematic science.

We advance more definitely into geographic study when we construct regions in terms of the integration of two or more elements. For example, we may recognize taiga regions as based on the interrelation of certain characteristics of climate, residual soil materials, and vegetation; or terraced vineyard districts based on the interrelation of steep slopes of well-drained soil in areas of light frost climates and west European culture.

Under this concept, the region is the areal expression of a logical generalization of process relationships, and hence a first step in the explanation of the geography of an area. Since certain types of partial integration repeat themselves in widely separated areas, this concept of region may also be used generically. But in most parts of the world even such partial integrations vary greatly over areas of considerable extent because of differences in the subsoil, in relative location, or in human culture. Consequently, it is generally not possible to cover the world satisfactorily in a regional division based on the integration of two or more elements.

In recent decades numerous students have sought to establish a concept of regions based primarily or exclusively on the interconnections of places. This development appears to have proceeded independently in different countries. One particular aspect, that of the "metropolitan region," was developed as early as 1917 by Fawcett in delineating "the provinces of England," as organized on metropolitan centers, and has been followed by Dickinson and Smailes [*93*:150–58]. In this country Wellington Jones and Robert Platt introduced the concept at a somewhat different level, emphasizing the functional organization of areas around local communities [*123*:22f.]. Through Ullman and Whittlesey, the difference between such a "nodal region" and the more familiar form of "uniform region" was expounded in the latter's chapter in *American Geography* on "The Regional Concept" [*4*:37–40].

In the meantime, various German geographers have been developing a similar contrast in concepts.[13] As early as 1923, Sidaritsch stated the contrast clearly and outlined the differences in criteria.[14] More recently Hans Carol has provided a particularly clear presentation of the contrast, and of the alternating use of the two concepts in research, distinguishing between "formal" (in the simple sense of "form") and "functional" regions [*31*:255–61].

Many of these contributions are discussed in a short but illuminating paper by G. W. S. Robinson in 1953 [*86*]. Independently of these writings, but in part dependent on the earlier work of Hettner and on *The Nature of Geography*, De Jong has presented the most thorough discussion of the comparison and relation of the two forms, which he distinguishes in terms of "vertical unity" and "horizontal unity" [*34*:13–21].[15]

[13] Overbeck provides a review and bibliography of this development [*40*].

[14] Marian Sidaritsch, "Landschaftseinheiten und Lebensräume in den Ostalpen," *Petermanns Mitteilungen*, Vol. LXIX (1923) , 257.

[15] The distinction is clearly defined and followed in De Jong's discussion, but it is possible to become confused, as he himself recognizes, since both concepts refer to areas and hence "horizontal" may appear to apply to both.

All of these studies describe essentially the same contrast in concepts, although the terminology varies and none of the terms appears entirely satisfactory. Clearly distinct terms are necessary, because the use of the two concepts as effective tools of research requires that they be sharply distinguished from each other, as Ullman and Philbrick have both noted [*123*; *109a*]. The contrast which needs to be expressed is that between approximate uniformity (in respect to certain phenomena) and approximate unity of organization (in respect to certain phenomena). For the former, "uniform region" claims too much, as Ullman notes [*123*:5]; "homogeneous" is essentially correct, but apparently may readily be misunderstood.[16]

For the latter, "nodal region," the term used in *American Geography*, emphasizes what is only a part, and not a necessary part, of the concept; more serious is Platt's objection that the term suggests a static picture rather than the dynamism of movement which is essential to the concept [*112*]. If we can accept the direct meaning of "formal," ignoring its more common connotation in English, the words "formal" and "functional," which are common to many languages, point directly to the contrast between the two concepts. They must not, however, be taken as describing the contrast but merely as pointing to it. We can distinguish between a "dairy region" and a "beef region" whether or not the difference is reflected in any concrete forms, but both are examples of formal regions. Further, the approximate uniformity of character of a formal region may be based on similarity of functional connections within each of many small units included in it—for example, a farming region where groups of farms have each a similar association with a farm village [cf. Uhlig, *48*:7]. In this case each of the farm villages with its associated farms constitutes a functional region of small size but intensive organization. Likewise, each such functional area con-

[16] In *American Geography* this term is applied to both concepts [*4*:21, 37], but only by making the word "homogeneous" synonymous with "unity"—as though one were to say that a steel ingot and a watch were both homogeneous. The confusion in communication that results is best demonstrated in the chapter on "Political Geography" in that volume, which follows the same usage in analyzing a political region in terms of "the two elements of homogeneity [read "unity"]: uniformity [read "homogeneity"] and "coherence" [*4*:179 f., 188–91]. Farther on in the same chapter, "homogeneity" is used in the normal sense of approximate uniformity [*4*:196–99].

sists of smaller parts, each of which is either a formal unit in itself—the village—or a part of a formal unit—a part of a cultivated valley or of a forested slope [cf. Carol, *32*:125].

None of these terms seems entirely satisfactory. The most accurate, to my mind, are "homogeneous" and "functionally organized," both of which are in some degree awkward. In the remainder of this discussion I have followed Carol and several other students in using the contrast of "formal" and "functional" regions.

Regions of functional organization may be determined by a single feature, as in the case of a river system, but in most cases one is concerned with different kinds of features in interrelation—for example, the integration of different types of production through transport routes and the media of trade. In any case, the unity of area involved is a reality based upon dynamic connections among phenomena at different places. The functional region is therefore not a descriptive generalization of character, but rather the expression of a theory of process-relationships, a generalization in the logical sense.[17] In this respect it is similar to a formal region based on elements in interrelation. But it differs in that it expresses a theory of spatial organization through interconnections across area.

In determining that an area is a functional region, the student is reconstructing an existing areal synthesis—limited, to be sure, to certain features of the area. Hence, in establishing the existence of a functional region as actuality, the student is completing an integral step in the geography of the area. Furthermore, in the degree to which an area is a functional unit, it constitutes a *whole*; for its unity has the structure of totality, or is more than the sum of its parts [*1*:265, 278–80; cf. De Jong, *34*:93]. Each specific functional region has its own particular size, shape, structure,

[17] Hettner noted [*2*:221, 224, 229, 345] and Lautensach has recently re-emphasized [*37*:11n.] the common use of "generalize" or "generalization" in two quite different meanings: (1) in the descriptive sense, in which it is necessary to generalize in textual or cartographic presentation, by describing characteristics true of the greater part of an area, regardless of variations or small exceptions; and (2) in the "logical" sense, by which we establish a generic concept to describe all phenomena having in common certain characteristics deemed significant, disregarding differences in characteristics of lesser importance.

and pattern of internal movements. In the respects in which it is a functional unit, but only in those respects, it represents an areal feature in reality, to be discovered and analyzed by the geographer. It is this fact which distinguishes the concept of the functional region from any other concept of region.

Functional regions can also be classified into generic types, as suggested by such generic words as farms, cities, states (in the sense of areas), hinterlands, or trade areas. But in each case the generic type depends not on certain features found throughout each area, but on the structure of the area.

The interconnection of places, unlike the character of places, is not universal, so that there is no reason to assume that a system of functional regions will cover all of any area under study. Where that is the case, as in areas of well-developed modern communication and trade, the reality of functional organization of areas is expressed by overlapping the functional regions. If for convenience of mapping or study one divides the area by sharp lines, this division must be recognized as a distortion of the reality of the geography of the area.

Functional regions at one level may be integral parts of a larger functional region at a higher level. In regions of government, there is, of course, a complete hierarchy of organization of areas, from the lowest level of minor civil division to the highest level of the independent state. Philbrick has demonstrated the existence in Northern Interior United States of a somewhat similar hierarchical system of regions of trade and service activities [109]. Any apparent similarity in the case of formal regions is fictitious: a system of major type regions, subregions, and sub-subregions is only the invention of the student, involving arbitrary judgments of what differences are considered as major or minor in determining the hierarchy [1:320–24].

Our discussion of the various kinds of formal and functional regions demonstrates that in either case we can establish objectively defined divisions of area only in terms of a limited part of the total complex of areal variation. In the simplest case, areas of a certain class, we are dealing with but one or two independent elements. Either formal or functional regions may be defined in terms of several integrated elements, but these cannot represent more than a partial integration. In other words, it is only in topical rather than regional studies that we can establish sharply and objectively defined regions. Further, experience has shown that regions thus defined are most useful in determining the degree of covariance among a limited number of elements, again in topical studies. It is a historical paradox that in seeking to establish technical concepts of regions as tools for research in regional geography, we have, in fact, constructed and used these concepts in topical studies.

It is therefore appropriate to ask ourselves whether tools which were perhaps designed to serve the purposes of regional study are well constructed for topical studies. In regional geography it is necessary to divide the total area under study, alloting every place to some region. Hence we seek to establish unitary regions, whether formal or functional, by division of the entire range of variations into classes, with the result that many places are included within one region which might almost as well be included in another. For the purposes of studying covariance of elements, in the search for generic relationships, we may anticipate much clearer conclusions if we establish distinctive types of homogeneity or coherence, including in the corresponding regions only those places that conform clearly to such restrictive criteria. Once we had established the nature of the relationships in such typical regions, we could go on to study the more difficult problem of relationships in areas which did not fit into clear-cut types, whereas under our present use of the regional method in topical studies, these marginal or transitional areas tend to confuse the relationships in typical areas. This is particularly true in cases in which such areas of doubtful classification are not simply intermediate in degree between two types, but represent rather a combination of two or more types—as, for example, a ridge-and-valley area which is not, like many hill areas, intermediate in degree between mountains and plains, but rather may be an areal combination of typical small plains and typical mountains.

Likewise, in designing a division of area for regional study, we seek to find a single system of classes or types for each of the features used as critical determinants of the division. Such a system must be based on all the significant relationships of the feature concerned to the other variable features of area. Carrying this purpose over into topical studies, we have long sought to establish a standard system of climatic regions, or of soil regions, etc., of major areas or of the world. But we know that the significance of variations (in rainfall, for example) varies greatly for different features, whether wild vegetation, crop systems, human physiology, or sea or air navigation. We could expect more significant results if we abandoned the idea of standard systems of regions and sought rather to construct in each topical study types specifically designed for the particular integration under study.

Finally, there remains the question of whether we can utilize the concepts of formal and functional regions, established in studies of very partial integrations, to construct a division of area suitable for the study of the maximum complex of interrelations in areas in regional geography. This would be possible on an objective basis only if all the elements interrelated at any place formed a single integration, varying in constant interrelationship from place to place, and if all the interconnections of elements at different places formed functional regions coinciding in location and extent.

That the facts of areal variation do not fit this pattern was clearly recognized by Whittlesey's committee in its study of the regional concept [4:44]. As a compromise, however, that would make it possible to include most of the content of area that is of concern to geographers, the committee urged the use of a new concept, the "compage," which is limited to "all the features of the physical, biotic and societal environments that are functionally associated with man's occupance of the earth" [4:45]. The "compage," if I understand the concept correctly, is thus considered as a highly complex but unified element-complex.[18]

But does "man's occupance of the earth" in any area constitute a single totality? In criticizing certain conclusions in *The*

[18] In the absence of any statement of what is included under "man's occupance of the earth," it is not clear that this would exclude much or any of what is included in geography as a whole in terms of the definition developed in this paper—the study of "the variable character of the earth shell as the home of man."

Nature of Geography, De Jong correctly observes that man cannot be considered as functioning in terms of a single totality;[19] we distinguish between the "economic man," the "political man," and the cultural or social man. His attitudes and purposes in these respective fields may be quite independent of each other, but in terms of such attitudes he produces independently areal variations in economic existence and action, in the phenomena of political geography, or of social geography [*34*:31]. Indeed, within even a limited area, men differ in attitudes and purposes of economic life, with consequent areal variations in part independent of each other.

In actual practice in regional studies, as we observed earlier, we must use interchangeably the division of total integration into segments of partial integrations and the division of area into regional parts. In doing this we may make use of a variety of divisions into formal regions, each based on one or more elements or element-complexes, and a variety of divisions into functional regions, each based on different kinds of interconnections of places. To some extent these may correspond in area, suggesting the existence of integration at a higher level; on this basis we may be able to recognize restricted portions of the total area as distinctive core regions in terms of a high degree of integration.

Lack of correspondence is, however, more common. When one element of areal variation is closely related, as a causal factor, to the areal variations of two or more other elements, it is seldom that variations in the first case have equal effects on each of the others. Hence, between any two core areas of marked homogeneity in form there is commonly a wider belt in which correspondence is lacking, representing an area of marked heterogeneity.

Certain elements, notably climatic elements, tend generally to vary gradually over area, whereas others, such as landforms, may vary either gradually or very sharply. The patterns of certain other elements, such as those of mineral deposits or of

[19] While the writer agrees with De Jong's conclusion on this point, and agrees also that it renders impossible from the start any attempt to construct a single regional division of the world on the basis of cultural element-complexes, as is attempted in that work [*1*:330], it is fair to note that the failure of such an attempt was recognized in the original conclusion. [*1*:361].

cultural heritage, show little or no correspondence with climate or landforms. For all features which are dependent on connections through space, we must expect a lack of correspondence because location (distance) varies greatly in importance for different features. Finally, we cannot expect correspondence between regions based on homogeneity and those based on functional organization; indeed, to some extent we must expect the opposite, because of the tendency for areas differing in production to be closely associated in trade [*1*:441f.; *34*:85].

Hence, when the student combines all the various patterns of formal and functional regions to produce a single organization of unit-areas as the framework of his study, he is compelled to make a large number of compromises among incommensurable patterns.[20] By patching together, as he must, varied portions of many formal and functional regions, each in terms of particular categories, he has constructed divisions of area which are neither formal nor functional regions. All that can be claimed is that each has some degree of formal or functional unity, or both, in respect to some categories, at the sacrifice of formal and functional unity in respect to other categories. He has, however, constructed divisions of the total area, each of which, in a different way and a different degree, he may consider more or less as a distinct unit [cf. De Jong, *34*:57f.]. In short, he has attained to the utmost possible—in view of the complexity of the problem and the need of including all parts of the area in some division—the concept expressed by the word "region" in common usage. No technical concept has been established.

The compromises of judgment by which these regions were constructed depend, and should depend, on the point of view of the student and the particular purpose of his study [cf. Cholley, *52*:25–53]. They can be assumed to be useful only for him and his

[20] In the attempt to avoid a major part of this problem, some students choose to ignore, or appear to ignore, the patterns formed by features involving man, and to divide the area into so-called natural regions. We need not repeat here that these can only be "regions based on natural conditions as significant to man," that their construction therefore involves essentially the same problems of compromises among incommensurable patterns, and that the problem is commonly resolved by mere omission of the more difficult, though critical, elements [*1*:296–300; similarly, De Jong, *34*:44–46].

study; the construction of such a regional framework, however useful and necessary a step in his study, cannot be considered in itself a contribution to knowledge.

We find, therefore, that professional geographers use the word "region" for several different concepts. The concept of an area homogeneous in particular categories, the formal region, and the concept of an area coherently organized in particular ways, the functional region, are concepts of partial integration—the topical approach. For the concept of a unit of areal division in regional study, we use the word "region" in essentially its original and common meaning.[21]

COMPARISON WITH OTHER FIELDS

It is often, but erroneously, supposed that geography is unique in using two apparently opposing forms of organization. We noted earlier the close parallel with anatomy. The more or less comparable situations in astronomy, human history, and particularly historical geology are discussed at some length in *The Nature of Geography* [1:408–13]. If the greater part of the work in botany may be organized on a "systematic" basis, that does not mean that botanists do not use the regional approach. But studies which are concerned less with plant associations as such, and more with the interrelations of plants in areas—the vegetative

[21] The discussion of the same problem in German geography occupies a major part in current methodological papers of German geographers. German usage offers two words, *Land* and *Landschaft,* which may be used more or less as we use the word "region," but *Landschaft* in addition carries the meaning of our word "landscape." German geographers recognize at least four distinct concepts of regions: either formal or functional regions, and in each case, either generic (types) or specific regions. *Landschaft* is evidently the preferred term and a large number of German geographers are in agreement that the core of geography is the study of *Landschaften,* but few of them are in agreement on which of the several concepts of region shall be called *Landschaft* (compare the studies cited by Lautensach, Schmitthenner, Troll, Schmithüsen, Carol, Bobek, and Uhlig). While the discussions of the German writers help to illuminate our own problem, they offer no solution for it. In both cases it would appear that since each of the several concepts involved is important in geography, the solution must be found not in attempting to restrict either "region" or *Landschaft* to one precise meaning, but rather to recognize each as a very general concept, using additional words to name more precise and technical concepts.

cover—are scarcely to be distinguished from plant geography.[22]

The type of research activity in which the theoretical contrast between the two approaches is of greatest practical importance is in government agencies where students work in organized groups to supply intelligence concerning conditions throughout the world. Some insist that such work must be organized in terms of economic, psychological, political, and strategic problems, with but secondary consideration for location, whereas others are no less convinced that the only reasonable basis is a division by major areas and countries in order to secure an integrated picture of all these elements as they actually exist in each area. Caught in the midst of such a controversy during my war service in Washington, I was surprised to realize that my highly academic discussions of this theoretical question had an important practical application. Not that I could derive therefrom a definitive solution of the practical problem facing the agency, but that I could persuade my contending colleagues that both sides were right, and both were wrong—that there was no simple logical solution to the problem. What was needed was an organization divided regionally at one level and topically at different levels, so as to facilitate combining the two approaches in varying degrees as needed in each particular piece of study.

SUMMARY

The contrast expressed by the terms "systematic" or "general" geography versus "regional" geography is not that of a division of geography into two halves; neither is it a contrast between two distinct methods of study used separately, the one in some studies, the other in others. Regardless of the extent of area under study, we are concerned to analyze an extremely complex integration of phenomena which varies over area in an extremely complex manner. To break this dual complexity down to more

---

[22] Minor semantic confusion results from the fact that among botanists the study of the distribution of plants, as species and genera, is often called "plant geography." On the general principle that in names composed of two or more words the major emphasis is on the noun, commonly the final word, one would suppose that any subject whose title ends in the word "geography" was a part of the field of geography.

manageable form, it is necessary in any study in geography to use two different methods of analysis in varying degrees and inter-changeably—analysis of segments of integration and analysis by sections of area.

We break down the total complexity of integration formed by phenomena interrelated in place and interconnected between places by topical division into segments, each consisting of a less complex and closer integration, and we break down the complexity of areal variation by regional division into areal units, each including a restricted range in the variation of the segment of integration under study and a closer interconnection of the phenomena among places. The greater the degree of topical division, the less the degree of regional division necessary, and with the increasing complexity of the topical segments the finer must be the regional division. Geographic studies do not fall into two groups but are distributed along a gradual continuum from topical studies of the most elementary integration at one end to regional studies of a most complete integration at the other.

What particular division of the total topical integration will provide segments showing the closest integrations cannot be determined by any standard system, such as the classification of phenomena among the systematic sciences. Nor will a single standard system of regional division provide areal units of minimum variation of the integration to be studied. Each must be determined for each particular study by preliminary examination of the area through the opposite approach, and this alternation of method continues through successive stages of the study.

Both methods of approach therefore utilize the regional method, that is, the division of the total area under study into sections, each having a maximum degree of unity, whether of character or of coherent organization or of both. But whether one is using at the moment the topical or the regional approach, one can make most effective use of different concepts of regions.

In using the topical approach it is most effective to use regions that are objectively defined in terms of either partial integration of phenomena in place (formal regions) or partial interconnection of phenomena among places (functional). In either case such regions may be studied as specific regions or as generic types.

The latter will be most useful if defined in restricted terms (even though such a system fails to provide complete coverage of area) rather than in classes which provide a category for all places.

In using the regional approach it is necessary to combine the objectively defined concepts listed above in a variety of ways and to modify the criteria to include every place in the area under study in one region. The regions thus established vary in the basis of regional unity and necessarily involve subjective judgments in definition and delimitation. Consequently, this concept of region cannot be defined more narrowly than the common meaning of the word, indicating an area which in some particular way is distinctive from other areas. The regional division of an area on this basis must be tailored to the purposes of the particular study, and cannot be assumed to be suitable for any other study of the area.

The contrast between the two approaches is not peculiar to geography, but is found, in differing form, in many other fields. The simplest analogy is that with anatomy, in which sections of the human organism are comparable to regions. But the situation is perhaps most similar to history, if we think of periods as the historical counterpart of regions in geography.

The comparison of the two methods of approach raises questions concerning the extent to which each can be applied in studies seeking to establish generic concepts and principles rather than to analyze individual cases. This is a question of the first order of magnitude in current thought in geography, and will be considered in the next chapter.

X.

Does Geography Seek to Formulate Scientific Laws or to Describe Individual Cases?

OF ALL THE PROBLEMS of current concern in the thinking of geographers, the most disturbing appears to be the question whether geography "like other sciences" can develop "the knowledge of principles, laws, and general truths"—and thus lay claim to the name of science—or whether its function is merely to describe innumerable unique areas [*124; 125*].

PAST DEVELOPMENT IN THE FIELD

That geography has always shown a great concern for individual cases is an empirical fact clearly observable in the literature. That literature also demonstrates from earliest times a concern to construct generic concepts and general principles. Since the eighteenth century geographers have had increasing success, varying in degree in different branches, in developing such concepts and principles.

Which of these two concerns represents the ultimate purpose of geography? The methodological answers which different students have given to this question are less informative than an empirical judgment of their substantive works.

Thus, Ritter in his theoretical essays said that he was concerned to explain particular cases, *die Besondere,* in order that a great accumulation of such cases would make possible the construction of systematic principles [22:75]. But the fact that he devoted most of his life to the study of individual areas and for that purpose undertook many generic topical studies, was a reversal of his theory [1:74].

Humboldt appears to have regarded generic studies—the search for general principles that would lead to understanding of the unity of all reality—as a higher level of scientific study than the analysis and interpretation of individual areas. Yet his generic studies, important as they were in their time, are today of little value, and the over-all work in general geography (as part of cosmography), with which he intended to crown his career, the *Kosmos*, contributed relatively little even in his day, whereas the studies he made of particular areas where he worked in the field remain of lasting value [1:82; *129*].

Even in the study of particular categories of phenomena—as in the study of mountains, for example—geographers have been concerned not merely to study different types, but to present full description and the maximum of interpretation of individual cases. In regional studies their concern is not simply to find further raw material for generic concepts or a testing ground for principles or laws, but rather to analyze the specific over-all complex of phenomena of each area.

In sum, what the world evidently expects of geography, and geographers endeavor to supply, is an explanatory description of phenomena and the total complex of phenomena that constitute area, both of regions of the world, each considered for its own interest, and of the world as a whole.

Many students of geography are distressed to see that so much of the work in their field is concerned with the study of individual cases. Comparing this situation with that in many other fields of science, they conclude that geography is deficient in scientific character because a large part of its work does not lead to the formulation of scientific laws.

That such considerations are far from new is shown by Wagner's discussion in 1880 of articles questioning "the scientific character of geography." Wagner found that these critics presumed, erroneously he felt, that the goal of science (*Wissen-*

schaft[1]) was the discovery of laws. Others, however, held that geography was in part like "history and philology" in its concern for individual cases. Geography was a part of natural science, utilizing scientific laws, but these could not possibly cover the content of geography. A large part of the discussion has a familiar ring.

The importance of individual cases is most obvious in the study of particular areas. Although a large number of studies of individual regions have been contributed to geographic literature in the seven or eight decades since Wagner wrote, these have not permitted the formulation of any laws of regions. Some writers, however, urge that we should have faith, that sometime, somehow, the accumulation of all these independent studies will enable some geographer to construct and demonstrate scientific laws of regions [*1*:378–97, 451, and 1i].

If this were the purpose of regional studies, it would be necessary to develop standard methods of delimiting regions and of analyzing the complex integration of areal variations contained in each region. In discussing this problem in the previous chapter we found that efforts in this direction are successful only to the degree to which studies are limited to partial integrations; as we approach the full complexity of integration presented by reality, any system breaks down. Nevertheless, we continue to be concerned to describe, and as far as possible comprehend, the reality of areal variation in terms of nearly complete integration of phenomena. Judged by what it does, geography is evidently concerned to attain the maximum understanding of individual areas, whether or not it can attain scientific laws about regions.

This situation is not unique to geography. In considering the philosophy of science in general, Windelband and Rickert,

[1] American scholars of eminent standing have found confusion in the use of the German word *Wissenschaft*, whereas in reality the difficulty arises from our usage, peculiar to very recent times, of the word "science" [*1*:367]. The dilemma which Wagner reported in German thought in 1880 (in *Geographisches Jahrbuch*, Vol. VIII, 523–89) has evidently been resolved by keeping the word *Wissenschaft* to its original meaning but rejecting the definition based on the search for laws. In this country, under the domination of natural scientists, the tendency has been to accept the definition and thus force a change in the meaning of our "science," originally identical to *Wissenschaft*, to something seldom clearly defined.

more than half a century ago, distinguished between the study of situations that are repeated in essentially the same form in large numbers of cases, as "nomothetic," and the study of the specific character of individual cases, as "idiographic." It may facilitate understanding if we speak more simply of generic studies in contrast to studies of individual cases.[2] It is necessary also to avoid a confusion which the authors of these terms introduced in attempting to classify the different fields of science in terms of these concepts. While it is true that there are marked differences among the sciences in the relative importance of generic versus specific studies, both forms are of importance in nearly all fields of science (not including mathematics) [1:379; similarly, Lautensach, 37:8f.].

The fact that geography is one of the fields of knowledge in which a comparatively large amount of effort is spent in studying individual cases rather than constructing scientific laws has been a matter of concern to critics within our midst for more than half a century. Before concluding that drastic changes are in order, it will be well to consider to what degree this may be a necessary consequence of the nature of our subject. It should be helpful to consider what conditions, in science in general, facilitate or make difficult the establishment of generic concepts and principles and, on the other hand, what conditions make it positively desirable to seek maximum knowledge concerning individual cases. By comparing these general conditions with those peculiar to geography we should be better able to understand what is possible and desirable in our field.

DIFFICULTIES IN ESTABLISHING SCIENTIFIC LAWS

In all branches of science the ability to establish generic concepts and scientific laws of high reliability and utility is dependent on

[2] Literally, the term "nomothetic" refers to the search for general laws, as opposed to "idiographic," the intensive study of an individual case, but I agree with Ackerman that any generic concepts, whether or not leading to scientific laws, should be considered as contrasted with "idiographic" as the intensive study of the individual case [96]. In translating the latter term (which is not to be confused with "ideographic"), I have found that to speak of the study of "unique cases," though correct in the sense that every case is unique, may be misleading in suggesting the sense of "rare" or "unusual."

(1) the number of identical or essentially similar cases available for examination and classification, (2) the relative simplicity of the complex of independent or semi-independent factors found in interrelationship, and (3) the degree to which interpretation requires analysis of factors which are beyond our ability to analyze.

1. In most of the natural sciences and in a few of the social sciences the student has available an almost unlimited number of cases of the same phenomenon. More correctly, one may generalize only very loosely for a single field. In astronomy, geology, economics, and demography there are some aspects in which the student may find a very large number of similar cases but others in which the number is extremely small.

The student of any branch of biology, including human physiology, has a special advantage resulting from the nature of genesis of living things. All specimens of a given species, though differing in some degree among themselves, are nearly identical in a wide range of essential characteristics. But when the biologist seeks to explain the evolution of a particular species, he is involved in a problem of the unique; a study of the evolution of other more or less similar species may offer suggestions but it does not provide identical cases—save to the extent that basic cellular processes are alike because of ultimately common origin.

These several conditions apply in greatly varying degree to different aspects of geography. As long as we are dealing with partial integrations at a relatively elementary level, we may find a large number of nearly identical cases. In plant geography and some aspects of agricultural geography we have also the advantage of dealing with specimens of biological species. In studying the relationships of domesticated plants and animals, however, our problem is complicated more than is commonly recognized by the varieties which man has developed, and continues to develop, from the same species.

When, however, we study more complex integrations in geography, we find a much smaller number of essentially similar specimens. As in many other sciences, we attempt to overcome this difficulty by recognizing categories or types within which differences in cases appear less marked than the similarities. But in thus classifying objects, or phenomena, each of which involves a host of independent or semi-independent elements, we do not have specimens that are similar in all essential elements. They are similar only in terms of the particular categories we have chosen, and may differ notably in other respects which research may demonstrate to be no less important. It is a common but serious error to assume that the establishment of a "type" provides assurance of the extent and degree of similarity which can be expected among the specimens of a species [*1*:325; similarly, Lautensach, *37*:6f.].

We face, therefore, a difficult dilemma: in order to study a sufficient number of areas as similar, we must define the category so broadly as to include individual variations sufficiently great as to upset the validity of generalizations based on the assumption of identical character; if the types are defined sufficiently closely to avoid this danger, we may have but one specimen of each type.

2. Generic relationships can most readily be established when one is dealing with a small number of independent variables, all subject to similar laws. More complex relationships may be resolved in those fields in which it is possible to conduct laboratory experiments in which most factors can be kept constant while selected factors are permitted to vary.

In studying the integration of phenomena in geography, even if limited to those of natural phenomena, we are concerned with highly complex situations which we must observe without means of control. In discussing this problem a century ago, Humboldt described how such complex integrations must be divided into less complex partial integrations, for each of which we should anticipate, with the advance of science, greater ability to establish laws of relationships. But between groups of very heterogeneous elements there would always, he believed, be gaps for which no laws would be applicable [*14*:65–68].

Humboldt's consideration of the problem of complexity was focused on phenomena in nature. If we consider a problem in geography in which the work of man, in groups and as an individual, constitutes an important factor, the complexity becomes vastly greater [cf. Le Lannou, *59*:136ff.].

In one respect to be sure, the complexity of elements in the social sciences permits partial integration into restricted types, each composed of a large number of elements, through the concept of a common social heritage. But the analogy suggested by the term is far from complete. In comparison with the classes, orders, families, subfamilies, genera, and species of the biological classification, all human cultures represent varieties of a common species—or, at most, of closely related species of the same genus. Through migration and transmission of ideas, different cultures intermingle in a great variety of ways, so that there are always important differences in social heritage in different places, and even among different groups and individuals in the same place.

3. To the extent that the phenomena studied in the social sciences are determined by the combined actions of large numbers of people, it may be possible to analyze the human factors in terms of generic characteristics, forces, and responses. Undoubtedly, this is true of much of the work in geography. Given the natural conditions of the Northern Interior of the United States, the cultural background of the European settlers, the addition of culture goods acquired from the Indians, and the economic conditions of the world at the relevant period, we may feel competent to explain why and how there developed the particular type of land use which we associate with the Corn Belt. We might similarly explain the development of Chicago, reasoning that had the particular persons who actually first started that center gone elsewhere, other persons would undoubtedly have attempted to utilize its outstanding advantages for trade, and would no doubt have succeeded. But such a line of reasoning will not account for an Indianapolis, a Munich, or an Akron; neither is it adequate to explain the unusual character of the agriculture of the Annapolis-Cornwallis Valley.

Geographers have commonly tended to discount cases of the latter kind as exceptions, to consider the character of development of most places as resulting from a multiplicity of human reactions in which individual peculiarities are lost in the average [cf. Bowman, 5:31]. Even if this were true of the general development of areas, we must recognize that the more detailed and precise the study, the more important are the particular decisions and actions of individual persons. But even on the more generalized scale our traditional assumption overlooks the important influence which individual persons may exert on the motivations and actions of hundreds or millions of other people, with resultant consequences of major importance in the geography of areas, small or large. The face of Europe today would certainly be different if Julius Caesar had not survived his Caesarean birth, or if Martin Luther had been killed by the lightning which struck him at the age of twenty-two. Thousands of lesser figures have influenced small and large communities, and thereby left the mark of their leadership on the geography of every country, even if their names are no longer known.[3]

THE PROBLEM OF DETERMINISM

In seeking to develop scientific laws by means of which we may explain the phenomena studied in the social sciences, including all aspects of geography in which man is a factor, we encounter a major theoretical difficulty which is controversial and a practical difficulty concerning which there can be little question. Can the actions of individual human beings be considered as theoretically determinable by inexorable, unvarying scientific law, and if so, can we ever hope to know enough of these laws and of the conditioning factors to be able to demonstrate their operation in specific cases?

No doubt we can all agree with Hettner that science will not allow the concept of free will to deter it from seeking to determine the causes of human actions to the utmost of its ability [2:209, 227; *13*]. The increasing ability of modern psychology to explain the reactions of human beings to stimuli, as demonstrated in the majority of cases, has led many students to suppose that all decisions and actions of individuals are ultimately susceptible to scientific determination. Even if the laws of human psychology had attained a degree of certainty and completeness comparable to that of, say, the physiology of monkeys, such a hypothesis would be comparable to saying that a hyperbola is sure to reach its asymptote. In reality the established laws of human psychology

---

[3] Hettner's discussion of the problem, *Gesetzmässigkeit und Zufall* in geography, recognizes this difficulty, but, to my mind, tends to underestimate its quantitative importance [*13*:2–15].

can as yet explain but a small part of all the decisions and actions of human beings—even the asymptote is still beyond our horizon. Hence, to assert that "science" has refuted, or could expect to refute, the possibility of some degree of free will would be to pretend to know what we cannot know.

Many scientists who recognize that science cannot demonstrate the hypothesis of scientific determinism nevertheless adhere to it as an article of philosophical faith to be defended as the foundation on which the whole structure of science depends. Any suggestion of doubt, any assumption of the possibility of free will, must therefore be attacked with wrath and scorn as unscientific [similarly, William James, as quoted by Platt, *111*:129f.].

Discussing this question a half-century ago, Chamberlin concluded that scientists who thus insisted upon determinism were inconsistent both in principle and in behavior. The most basic concept of science, he noted, is the assumption that we are not only capable of detecting error and of demonstrating truth but have also sufficient "volitional command over ourselves" to choose between truth and error. The assumption of determinism would not grant us this measure of choice. Commenting on the rhetorical wrath which Huxley had poured on a critic of his exposition of determinism, Chamberlin observed that "if determinism be true, I do not see how Huxley's critic could have swerved by a turn of a phrase from what he wrote, and Huxley's wrath was not more consistent than that assigned to Xerxes when he lashed the stormy Hellespont because it thwarted his purpose" [*6*:485, 486].

Now that physicists have learned to live with the ultimate inexplicability and uncertainty of the actions of individual electrons,[4] psychologists and social scientists—who have never even approximated absolute certainty in their work—need not be frightened by what is after all but a minor qualification, quantitatively speaking, of the basic assumption on which they work.

---

[4] The significance of these developments to our general concept of science had not, so far as I can judge, entered into Hettner's consideration of the question of determinism, even as late as 1935 [*13*]. It was ably discussed in an essay by Lehman in 1937, *"Der Zerfall der Kausalität und die Geographie"* [*1*:310], and more recently by Montefiore, a philosopher, and Williams, a geographer [*84*]. Most geographers will, no doubt, find less difficulty in understanding the briefer presentation by Emrys Jones [*74*].

As Montefiore and Williams express this: "there is no reason why one should not include among the alternative or absolute necessary 'parts' of a sufficient condition (in any situation involving human beings) a 'free act of choice'" [84:10]. The degree of uncertainty thus accepted is far less than the margin of our present inability to determine all the causes of individual human actions. We end always with an important degree of uncertainty, and whether we ascribe this in part to the possibility of "free will" or entirely to our lack of complete knowledge of the law governing human behavior in general or of the facts in particular cases, our explanation is no more and no less incomplete.

Whatever position one takes on the theoretical question, the practical problem remains. As Platt reminds us, acceptance of the theory of scientific determinism would bring the scientist no closer to his goal; there would always be a critical area beyond his reach [111:127–29]. Thus, in order to explain fully by scientific laws of cause and effect a single decision of any single human being, we would need to know all the factors of his biological inheritance and all the influences which molded his character from infancy on—far more data than we could ever hope to secure. Further, if the necessary data concerning all the factors involved were somehow made available, and we had established scientific laws explaining the interrelationships of these factors, what method would we have for integrating such a multiplicity of diverse laws involving many incommensurable factors? Finally, if both the impossible difficulties were overcome, so that we could reduce all the factors to common measure and express the total complex in mathematical form, that equation would be so complex as to be beyond solution by finite minds.[5]

Fifty years ago, when physical scientists generally accepted the doctrine of determinism, the geologist Chamberlin pronounced it a metaphysical assumption which could be justified as a hypothesis of science only if it could "be put into workable form, and carried into effect in all its applications, with every step true to the primary assumptions." If this could not be done, as he clearly doubted, "let it be cast aside like any other

[5] This last consideration, as stated in *The Nature of Geography* [1:433], should have been noted as received from the philosopher Charles Hartshorne.

unworkable hypothesis. Whatever metaphysicians may think of an unworkable scheme, scientific investigators may as well send it to the junk-shop" [6:483, 486]. Since the hypothesis appears even less workable today than when Chamberlin wrote, we agree with Montefiore and Williams that the issue of determinism versus free will has no practical relevance for geography [84:11]; it is a question of philosophical faith which has no place in scientific discussion [1:310].

The practical conclusion we must draw is that, whether because some degree of free will is a reality or because we can never hope to know fully the factors and processes that determine individual human decisions, there will always remain a hidden area in any study in social science which cannot be explained by scientific laws. The explanation of any problem in human geography by use of scientific principles will fall short of completion at the point where it is necessary to interpret the motivations and resultant decisions of particular persons. A large number of phenomena important to man can never be fully explained in terms of antecedent causes because the essential factors are inevitably lost from our knowledge. Even in the physical branches of geography, the same conclusion holds for those phenomena that have been in part produced by the action of man.

THE NEED FOR THE STUDY OF SPECIFIC CASES

One of the greatest differences among the fields of science, and within any one field, is the degree to which it is considered desirable to attain maximum knowledge concerning individual cases. In the development of the basic sciences in the nineteenth century this question hardly arose. The laws found to control the actions of a particular kind of molecule or subatomic particle (force) were believed to control every such elementary form of matter. Even today, when it is recognized that chemical laws are statistical expressions of probabilities based on the total behavior of many electrons of which the actual behavior of any one cannot be determined, most chemists, other than nuclear scientists, can continue their research undisturbed by the erratic variations of individual cases. Likewise, in most fields of biology individual variations from the norm of the species may be dismissed as of slight importance, but the geneticist is very much concerned with the unique cases of mutations. In short, as Allix states, "the only true determinism is statistical determinism" [49:301].

Such a limited form of determinism, which accounts for phenomena with a high degree of probability, is adequate only when one is concerned with totals of large numbers of individual cases. But in many aspects of science it is important to know and understand individual cases. The most reliable mortality tables can provide no answer to the age-old question of "how long have I to live?"

In certain fields, whether of the natural or social sciences, a limitation to generic studies would exclude large portions of their present content. Consider astronomy, a field whose "scientific" character is beyond question. The fact that there are many moons in our solar system, and presumably countless numbers in others, does not lessen the intellectual desire of man to learn more than the great amount which astronomers have already learned concerning the one moon which occupies so impressive a place in our sky—and which, since this sentence was first written, has suddenly assumed potentialities of great practical importance for all of us. The importance attached to the study of specific cases in such fields as geology or political science has been discussed before [1:380f.], and need only be mentioned here. Likewise no discussion is needed of the importance of the individual case in the study of history.

THE NECESSITY FOR
GENERIC AND SPECIFIC STUDIES IN GEOGRAPHY

That geography is a field of knowledge which is concerned to know and understand individual cases follows directly from its function as the study of places. The concept of place, like that of person or event, is in its essence a concept of the specific. In the previous chapter we found that the concern for the individuality of places is fundamental to the purpose of geography. But we cannot know, and could not comprehend if we did, the infinite variety of all possible places in the world. In order to know and comprehend not only many places but also the world as a whole, we must pursue both generic and specific studies.

The very fact that geography is concerned to comprehend the variations and interrelations of an unlimited number of places, each formed by a complex of an almost unlimited number of interrelated elements, imposes upon it the necessity of constructing generic concepts and principles. The primary advantage is the enormous saving of time and effort that results from the reduction of a vast number of individual features to an organized system of types. By using a single word or phrase designating a defined type, we can give a partial description of any one, or many, individual specimens.

Secondly, the comparison of areal distribution of the generic types of different categories of features may reveal patterns of covariance, suggesting hypotheses of interrelations, calling for studies of process relationships to establish theories, general principles, or laws. Or, conversely, a hypothesis of relationship developed by deduction or from the study of one or two cases may be checked by the comparison of areal patterns. The "universals" that have been established as proven principles or laws provide the only means by which an interpretation of relationship in a specific case can have a degree of reliability greater than that of intelligent, knowledgeable conjecture.

The application of any general principle to a particular case depends on generic concepts which fit the particular case only approximately. The attainment of the maximum degree of accuracy requires determination of the degree to which the particular conditions depart from the "norm" represented in each generic concept involved, and the consequences, in the process relationship, of those minor differences.

Hence, even in topical studies of features dependent solely on relationships among elements *in situ,* full comprehension of the individual feature ultimately requires an analysis of its unique characteristics. While there may be no need for such completely detailed knowledge in many cases, there are also a large number of places in the world for each of which we are concerned to know its individual particularities.

The problem is particularly difficult, as we noted earlier, in analyzing areal features which are in major part dependent on connections with features in other places. If such connections involve a limited number of elements and a limited number of other places—as in the case of an industrial plant dependent on a small number of specific areas for raw materials, power, and markets—we may be able to measure and combine the relationships involved (though not without a considerable margin of error), and on this basis establish certain type situations. Such studies approach, in theory at least, the simplicity of the situation with which astronomers have to work—a space occupied by unit objects widely separated and connected by the common force of gravitation. To some degree we approach this simple pattern also in the application of the central-place theory. More commonly in geography, however, we must think of location in reference to an almost unlimited number of other areas, and measured in terms of complex combinations of land and sea routes of variable ease or difficulty of transport for different kinds of connections.

History is under a comparable difficulty in terms of relationships through time. No period of time is like any previous period, not merely because of the differences in customs, technology, and institutions involved, but also and always because of the fact that any later period includes in its social heritage the consequences of any earlier period with which the historian might compare it.

The ultimate test in geography, of course, is in the study of the maximum complexity of areal variation over the earth. If we consider only minute places, selected at random or by some method of sampling, the complexity of each is so manifold, involving so many semi-independent elements, that we cannot expect, and do not find, sufficient degrees of over-all similarity to permit organization into generic types. Applying this conclusion in reverse, we must recognize that no matter what our method of "sampling," in most cases our minute places cannot be treated as true samples of larger areas.

In order to cover the world, therefore, we recognize as unit areas—"regions" in the general sense—pieces of area that are distinctive in varying respects (see Chapter IX). These regions are neither separate from each other, like the heavenly bodies, nor are they even rough approximations of clearly different total complexes, merging only by gradual transition into each other like the colors of the rainbow. For in any one of them important features may be more closely interrelated with the total complex of a neighboring unit area than with that of the area in which they are included. In other words, these unit areas are neither objects nor phenomena but rather creations of the student's mind. Hence, any system of classification and hypotheses based upon them are dependent not on reality but on what is in the student's mind. The most that could be produced would be laws concerning the thinking of geographers about the areas of the earth—conclusions no doubt of interest to the geographers but hardly to anyone else [*1*:391–96, 440–46, 467].

THE USE OF GENERIC CONCEPTS AND PRINCIPLES IN GEOGRAPHY

Whether the purpose of any study in geography is to seek comprehension of the maximum integration in restricted individual areas or of partial integration over areas of the world considered generically, our ability to analyze and interpret the interrelations of phenomena requires the use of generic concepts. Hence, as Hettner asserted over fifty years ago, scientific advance in geography depends on the development of generic concepts and the establishment and application of principles of generic relationships [*11*:618; repeated in *2*:223].[6]

Ackerman has clarified this principle in the essay on fundamental research in geography which he presented at Harvard in 1957. In what appears to be deliberate understatement, he suggests that "a touch of universality always distinguishes fundamental research." We may paraphrase his exposition of this principle in somewhat more categorical form than the original. The purpose of fundamental research is to furnish "building blocks," materials which make further advance possible. Studies of individual areas are in major degree end-products; however significant or necessary in themselves, they commonly do not provide

[6] This conclusion is repeatedly emphasized in *The Nature of Geography* [*1*:383–91, 396, 431, 446f., 458]. Cholley expresses a similar view [*52*:52, 57ff.].

foundations for studies of other areas. It is in the search for universals, generic concepts as well as general principles which may be constructed from them, that we are pursuing fundamental research [96:17ff.].

Generic concepts and principles of relationship are not the inventions of science. Many of the ordinary nouns in our language are expressions of generic concepts, and the thinking of the common man includes a large number of theories of relationships between phenomena. This is particularly true of geography, concerned as it is with obvious facts of the world about us. To raise such thinking to the level of scientific knowing, it is necessary to establish generic concepts that can be applied with the maximum degree of objectivity and accuracy and to determine correlations of phenomena with the maximum degree of certainty. Both purposes can best be accomplished if the phenomena can be fully and correctly described by quantitative measurements and these can be subjected to statistical comparisons through the logic of mathematics.

In view of these general principles, applicable in varying degree throughout all fields of science, it does not appear overoptimistic to anticipate major advances in geography from the application of statistical methods to the study of correlations. Statistical methods, to be sure, have long been employed in the description of climatic conditions, of crop and animal production, and of trade, but such uses led to no advance in geography as long as the method was confined to separate categories of phenomena without being applied in the study of interrelations of different phenomena. But within the last decade or so a large number of geographers have tackled the problem of applying statistical methods of correlation to the study of interrelationships, with results which offer great possibilities for enhancing the scientific quality of work in geography.

This is not the place to review or judge these developments in detail, but attention may be called particularly to one line of advance. In most other fields statistical methods can be satisfactorily employed in a linear dimension, based on variation through time; in geography we are fundamentally concerned with areal variation, involving a base of two dimensions. This difficulty appears to be overcome by the concept of "statistical surfaces" and the specific methods devised for reducing the measurement of such surfaces to computations in a single line.[7]

It is characteristic that the introduction of new and valuable methods of study in any field should lead some enthusiasts to pronounce that all work must hereafter be pursued by these methods, and that whatever is not amenable to analysis through such methods is not worth studying. Similar demands in other fields, as in sociology, have led to continual and often embittered controversy which to the onlooker appears largely unnecessary. In a field in which the phenomena that may come under study run the full range from cabbages to kings, from rainfall to religion, it would seem absurd to assert that all that is worth studying can be fully and correctly described in quantitative terms, or, conversely, that whatever phenomena or areal variations can be described in quantitative terms are worthy of study in geography.

Statistical studies of covariance in geography have been limited, so far at least, to the first step in integration, the interrelationship between two variables. The generic method faces great difficulties, as we have seen, when we attempt to bring all the heterogeneous relationships of multiple factors into an integrated system of scientific laws. Yet geography cannot abandon its goal of comprehending, to the best of its ability, the complex of phenomena that exists in interrelation in place. As Humboldt concluded, "even though the complete goal is unattainable, the partial solution of the problem, the striving toward a comprehension of world phenomena remains the highest and eternal purpose of all research" [*14*:68].

For this purpose geography must seek wherever possible to develop and utilize generic principles. Where this method falls down because of the complexity of the feature under study, it may be possible to determine the component segments of the

---

[7] Bibliographical references to recent studies in the use of such techniques in geography may be found in Arthur H. Robinson and Reid Bryson, "A Method for Describing Quantitatively the Correspondence of Geographical Distributions," *Annals*, Association of American Geographers, Vol. XLVII (1957), 379–91, and in Harold H. McCarty, John C. Hook, and Duane S. Knos, *The Measurement of Association in Industrial Geography* (Iowa City: State University of Iowa, 1956), pp. 20–53.

feature by the study of its development through time—a form of genetic study—and we may then find that the composition of some, at least, of the isolated segments can be interpreted in terms of established generic principles. In other cases we may attain some degree of understanding by comparing the situation in several areas shown to be similar in specific respects and different in others—the method of comparative regional geography [*1*:447f.].

Even the study of a single area may suggest certain hypotheses that may be applicable elsewhere. Particularly useful for this purpose is an area of considerable homogeneity in most major features but with notable variation in certain other features; here reality has provided a control over many variables, permitting a kind of laboratory study of the relationships among the few that vary strongly within the area.

By these techniques experienced and imaginative students gain insight into the relationships involved, insights different in order but not in kind from the degrees of probability which are dignified by the name "scientific laws."

THE RELATIVE IMPORTANCE OF THE GENERIC AND THE UNIQUE IN DIFFERENT ASPECTS OF GEOGRAPHY

It is obvious from the previous discussion that there is much greater opportunity to develop generic concepts and principles in studies of restricted segments of integration, "topical studies," than in the study of more nearly complete integrations of areas, "regional studies." This fact may mislead one to identify generic studies with topical studies and idiographic studies with regional studies. Since the distinction between topical and regional is one of degree, such a conclusion is clearly in error. At whatever point one is working along the continuum from the most elementary integration to the most complex the student may be concerned in greater or less degree with both generic and individual results.

In seeking the closest approximation to truth possible to finite minds, geography is concerned to develop hypotheses of interrelations in partial integrations (for example, by measuring the areal covariance of phenomena in topical studies), which when tested through studies of process relationships, may be established as generic principles. These may then be used as a means of analyzing more complex areal integrations. But as we approach the maximum complexity of integration involved in the totality of areas, we become involved with a great number of incommensurable principles of interrelationships. Through genetic study of the development of the particular complex, or through comparative study of the few areas of similar character, we may be able to suggest possible hypotheses, but the description of what is involved in the complexity of the individual case can only be the subject of an individual study, for which general principles, beyond a certain point, will never be available.

Whatever degree of integration one studies—from topical to regional—it is pertinent for a student to have in mind from the start whether his purpose is primarily to develop generic conclusions or to examine an individual case. Studies of individual cases may have value beyond a knowledge of the particular areas studied if they are selected as samples more or less representative of many similar areas [*1*:452–56]. Or a student may wish to experiment with and demonstrate particular methods of regional analysis; for that purpose it may be advantageous to select an area in terms of its particular association of features, regardless of its importance in the world. If, however, the ultimate purpose is simply to provide maximum knowledge concerning an individual case, the validity of choice of area on which to expend valuable research time and publication facility will depend on the degree of human interest or need for knowledge of that particular area among the innumerable available areas of the world.

Since geography requires both generic studies and studies of individual cases—it is in part nomothetic, in part idiographic—there seems little point in attempting to measure the relative amount of the two types of studies. We can emphasize the need for increasing development of generic studies, as necessary both for more advanced generic studies and for studies of individual areas, without thereby lessening the importance of the latter as representing an essential means of attaining the end-purpose of geography, namely, knowledge and understanding of the world in which we live. Each student may place his own emphasis on that type of study which he himself is most interested to pursue, without supposing himself in conflict with the viewpoint here presented.[8]

On the basis of the interpretative knowledge gained from the application of principles of relationships established by generic studies, or hypothesized from genetic or comparative studies, geographers may hope to provide counsel as well as information pertinent to planning for the future. Certainly, as Bowman observed, they should be able to draw conclusions limiting the range of possible results; they may be able to provide greater assurance of continuance of trends than the mere fact that the trend exists [5:198].[9]

In numerous cases also geographers may have sufficient knowledge of the relationships involved to permit somewhat more positive "predictions."[10] But to assume that our anticipation of future developments was based on the degree of knowledge of all the cause-and-effect relationships involved which is implied by the term "scientific laws" would constitute unreasoning optimism in conflict with what we know concerning the complexity and individuality of the problems we study [1:385, 431–34; similarly, Platt, 111:128].

Does this conclusion mean that geography differs from all other sciences? While the success of any branch of science is often measured, in the popular mind at least, by the reliability of its predictions, prediction is not the purpose of science. Rather

[8] A number of critics of *The Nature of Geography* drew erroneous conclusions concerning the similar discussion in that work by attempting to judge from a few phrases or metaphors the degree of emphasis placed on either type of study, some indeed going so far as to assert that, as viewed in that work, geography was essentially idiographic, in spite of repeated statements to the contrary in that discussion [1:383–86, 396, 446, 466].

[9] The marked similarity between Bowman's statements of the limitations on the capacity of geography to predict and those on the same topic in *The Nature of Geography* makes it seem highly probable that in this instance I failed to note my source [1:431–34; cf. 5:17, 32, 186f., 198].

[10] In the discussion of this topic in *The Nature of Geography*, "prediction" is assumed to imply a high degree of certainty [1:433]. This restriction appears inconsistent with the view of science maintained in that work and contrary to general usage; any forecast based on scientific procedures is a "scientific prediction," and may be useful if the reliability is greater than chance.

it is that part of science, the seeking to know, that is always weakest because it seeks to know what cannot yet be observed. Hence it is always qualified by the assumption, which only the event can justify, that all factors presently involved have been accurately accounted for and will not change, and that no new factor will enter into the situation [*84*:5–9]. In any situation involving decisions of human beings we can be certain that such an assumption is very unreliable.

The ability to predict in science is not to be gained by striving to predict, as though it were a skill to be learned by trial and error, but is rather a by-product resulting from a high degree of completeness and certainty of scientific knowledge concerning what has been observed. It is a principle of science that we should not only strive to secure such knowledge in the maximum degree, but that we should evaluate to what degree we have attained it—that is, we should know what we do not know. Hence we may state as an essential rule in scientific prediction that any forecast of future circumstances should recognize the factors of uncertainty or unreliability included in it. This rule may even require us to recognize that predictions based on "scientific knowledge" known to be very incomplete and uncertain may be less reliable guides than the "hunches" of men of experience.

On the other hand, the geographer as a responsible member of society has an obligation to make his knowledge useful to society: to the extent to which his professional knowledge enables him to offer predictions of greater reliability than those who lack that knowledge, he should be ready to offer them. In doing so, as Gottschalk has said of the comparable case of a historian,[11] he is not talking outside his field, but rather is drawing a tentative conclusion within the field of geography.

COMPARISON WITH OTHER FIELDS

Throughout this chapter reference has been made repeatedly to comparable situations in other sciences. The conclusions indicated for each of these fields depend on the intrinsic character of

[11] Louis Gottschalk, "The Historian's Use of Generalization," in *The State of the Social Sciences,* ed. by Leonard D. White, The University of Chicago Press, 1956, pp. 436–50.

its subject matter. There are many fields, both in the natural and in the social sciences, that are in certain respects similar to geography [1:408–13].

The closest parallel would appear to be that between geography and history. One important difference must be noted: since the study of geography, of any one period, depends on differences in natural conditions over the earth to a much greater degree than the study of history of any one country depends on changes through time in natural conditions, geography has a much greater concern for natural features, whereas history (as recorded history) is largely confined to human phenomena. In consequence, certain branches of geography have been able to develop scientific principles to a much greater degree than has been possible in corresponding studies in history [1:384]. Kroeber, indeed, according to Anderson, finds that the quality of uniqueness in historical findings is so paramount as to prevent the historical approach as such from attaining to "laws" or general theory [97:133]. On the other hand, as Gottschalk demonstrates in the paper mentioned above, historians constantly depend on generic concepts and principles of relationship in explaining the complex phenomena of human history.

WHAT KIND OF SCIENCE IS GEOGRAPHY?

The conclusions reached in this chapter concerning the character of work in geography may distress those who fear, as David Linton puts it, "that some awful reckoning may find geography not numbered among the scientific elect" [78:9]. A number of French geographers, following Baulig, have asked, "La géographie est-elle une science?" and reached the unhappy answer: Yes and No—that is, in part Yes, in part No [50; similarly, Chabot, 51:320f.; and Hamelin, 57:13]. Isaiah Bowman drew a similar conclusion some twenty years ago. Accepting a traditional and restricted concept of "science," he concluded that geography was, and could hope to be, only in part "scientific" [5:21, 31, 224]. A generation earlier T. C. Chamberlin had drawn a similar conclusion concerning the earth sciences in general, including his own field of geology [6:477].

The conclusions of all of these writers depend, at least in

part, on the relative degree to which geography is an "exact science," or has been able to develop scientific laws, or has demonstrated the ability to predict. This is to define science in terms of achievement rather than in terms of its character. If we consider "science" not in the passive sense of "knowledge," more or less established but constantly subject to revision, but in the active sense of seeking to know, it is to be distinguished from other forms of "knowing" by methods which it uses in seeking to establish knowledge and understanding of reality [*1*:431].

One of the most important methods of accomplishing this purpose, undoubtedly, is the construction and application of scientific laws. But to assert, as some do, that the formulation of scientific laws is the end-purpose of science is to confuse the means with the end. Hettner characterized this dictum as a remarkable adherence to medieval scholastic realism [*2*:22]. Its ultimate motivation is to demonstrate a hypothesis which without demonstration is assumed as an article of faith: that all the phenomena of reality, including those of the decisions and actions of men, are ultimately explainable in terms of cause-and-effect relationships determinable by undeviating laws. As we found earlier, in the discussion of determinism, this is not a workable hypothesis in science, but rather a philosophical hypothesis incapable of proof. To make the demonstration of this hypothesis the goal of science is to make all science but the handmaiden of philosophy [*1*:378f.].

None of the students named above expresses this distorted view of science. But while recognizing that its purpose is to seek to know and understand the universe, with the maximum degree of reliability possible, they assume that the construction and use of general laws is not merely the most important means for this purpose but the *sine qua non* of scientific work. I see no logical objection to such a restricted definition of the term "science," and if it were generally applicable to most fields known by that term, geographers could not demand that the definition be changed to permit inclusion of their field. Neither could they make geography into a science without excluding a large part of the material now included within their field. We would have to rest content with Bowman's conclusion that geography is only in part scientific, and that no matter how much it may increase its scientific content, other parts of its work, which Bowman considered highly important, would remain undefined, but beyond science [5:31f., 224ff.].

The same conclusion, however, applies in varying degree to every field of science. Whereas nineteenth-century scientists confidently expected that all knowledge of reality should soon be organized under general laws, no field has been able to reduce all its findings to those terms nor can we now anticipate that that will ever be possible. Consequently, it would be necessary to apply Bowman's conclusion not only to all the social sciences, as he recognized, but also to certain aspects of the natural sciences, including major parts of astronomy and nuclear physics. Every field calling itself a "science" would therefore have to distinguish between its scientific parts and its nonscientific parts. But the portion of each field thus defined as nonscientific would have no positive definition, no rules or standards of study to distinguish it from such forms of knowledge as intuition, common sense, artistic perception, or personal judgment.

We would be much freer in attempting to determine the nature of geography as a field of "knowing" if we accepted a conclusion, credited by Anderson to James Spuhler, that "the word 'science' has no proper place in scientific discourse" and should be avoided as "a fetish word, assumed to have the magical property of imparting authority to loose discussion" [97:132]. What are the essential characteristics which geography shares with other fields in seeking to establish reliable knowledge of reality?

Geography seeks (1) on the basis of empirical observation as independent as possible of the person of the observer, to describe phenomena with the maximum degree of accuracy and certainty; (2) on this basis, to classify the phenomena, as far as reality permits, in terms of generic concepts or universals; (3) through rational consideration of the facts thus secured and classified and by logical processes of analysis and synthesis, including the construction and use wherever possible of general principles or

M

laws of generic relationships, to attain the maximum comprehension of the specific interrelationships of phenomena; and (4) to arrange these findings in orderly systems so that what is known leads directly to the margin of the unknown [1:374–78].[12]

These statements describe a form of "knowing" that is different from the ways in which we "know" by instinct, intuition, a priori deduction or revelation. It is a description which includes all parts of the fields which are commonly called "science," and for which we have no other term to distinguish them from other forms of "knowing." If we may use this description as an empirical definition of that term, we can replace the question, "Is geography a science?" by the much more useful question, "What kind of science is geography?"

Geography is a field whose subject matter includes the greatest complexity of phenomena, and at the same time is concerned more than most others with studies of individual cases—of the innumerable places of the world and of the unique case of the world itself. For both reasons geography is less able than many other fields to develop and use scientific laws, but nonetheless, like every other field, it is concerned to develop them as much as possible.

In similar manner we may consider a question raised early in this study, whether geography is concerned primarily with description as "mere description" or is concerned to seek explanations.

During much of the nineteenth century scientists assumed that it was possible to establish relationships of such absolute certainty as to justify the concept of cause and necessary effect. But today even in the most nearly exact sciences it is recognized that we never fully explain the ultimate cause of any phenomenon. The most we can achieve is a description of the

---

[12] Similar statements in *The Nature of Geography* were based on the writings of such students of science as Morris Cohen, Frederick Barry, Viktor Kraft, and A. L. Kroeber, as well as numerous geographers. Critics who have objected to a use of the term "science" which does not correspond with their own conception appear to have ignored this discussion.

relationship which is as complete and as certain as possible [cf. Radcliffe-Brown, as quoted in *111*:131].

Consequently, we may properly state that in all steps of the scientific process the function of the student is to "describe"— whether he is describing a phenomenon seen with the eye or measured by some machine method, or a process of interrelation of elements constructed in the imagination. We start with "observation"—sensory description, often assumed to be the sole meaning of "description." We proceed to "analysis"—the description of the several parts of what has been observed as they appear to be related to each other. Next we state a hypothesis of relationships among the elements and processes. If sound, we have arrived at a higher level of knowledge—"cognitive description" of the elements and interrelationships among them.[13]

It is inherent in the nature of the object which geography studies—the variable character of the earth shell in which we live— that it is relatively easy for us to observe, directly or indirectly, most of the features whose areal variations, in relation to each other, contribute to the total variation of area. But it is by no means easy, and in many cases impossible, to determine how they are related to each other. But until we know that, we have no clearly objective measure for determining what weight to give each of the differently varying features in the description of a total integration, which we can never actually describe in total.

A further impossibility is presented by the goal of describing the variation of this over-all integration over the entire earth. When we reduce the infinite number of different places to a finite number of regions, each in some degree distinctive, we then face the problem of determining what weight to give to each of the areal differences within each unit region.

In all such cases where objective measurement is not possible the attainment of the maximum comprehension will depend on the judgment and skill of the student. Effective description in geography therefore involves no small degree of art, not in the

---

[13] For much of the thought of this paragraph I am indebted to Professor William-Olsson of Stockholm, who was good enough to read a draft of this section and offer numerous useful comments.

sense of subjective impressions, but in the objective sense of discernment and insight based on knowledge of those relationships that can be known.

If then we understand the term "scientific description" to include both what is known and what can be inferred, both of phenomena and of the process relations and associations of phenomena, we may once again modify our statement of the purpose of geography to read: *the study that seeks to provide scientific description of the earth as the world of man.*

XI.

The Place of Geography in a Classification

of the Sciences

IN STATING HIS HYPOTHESIS of the position of geography among
the sciences, in 1905, Hettner did not propose a new definition of
the nature and scope of geography. On the contrary, he adhered
to the view he had expressed a decade earlier, in the initial
article of the first number of the *Geographische Zeitschrift,* which
he described as the view which the great majority of (German)
geographers had learned from Richthofen: "Geography is the
study of the earth surface according to its differences," or "the
study of the different areas of the earth surface . . . in terms of
total characteristics." In that initial essay he had also noted
briefly that "in view of the extraordinarily large number of facts
of the most manifold kinds" that form the material of study in
geography, many "had questioned the possibility and justification for uniting them in one discipline." But "if one examines
the different sciences comparatively, one finds that while the
unitary character of many is determined by the materials studied,
that is not true of all; in some the unity lies in the method of
study. Geography belongs to the latter group. As history and
historical geology study the development of man and of the
nature of the earth through time, so geography proceeds from the
viewpoint of areal diversity" [*8*:2, 8].

In his essay of 1905, then, Hettner elaborated on this thesis,
in effect testing the formulation of the nature and scope of geog-

raphy that had evolved in the course of its development in terms of a logical classification of the sciences in general.

STATEMENT OF THE CONCEPT

The following explanation is in major part based on Hettner's statement of 1905 [*11*:549–53; repeated with little change in *2*:114–17]. Since much of that has already been translated into English [*1*:140–42], here we shall try to amplify his explanation in a more idiomatic English. In addition, certain alterations are specifically indicated.

Empirical knowledge is concerned with phenomena of many different kinds which occur in complex interrelationships, at specific times in history and at specific places in space. The ultimate purpose is to attain knowledge, description, and explanation of the whole, in all the complex interrelations, in all the differences from time to time and from place to place. But we cannot study everything at once, nor can any one student or group of students attain the competence necessary to analyze all the different kinds of problems that are involved. Hence the arbitrary division of the actual unity of knowledge into fields, disciplines, or compartments, in each of which a group of students concentrate their training and studies to secure the advantages of specialization.

One method of selecting a field for specialization is to pick a particular category of phenomena and concentrate study on that category. The particular phenomena are studied either independently of their interrelations in space and time with other phenomena, or those interrelationships are studied primarily in terms of their significance to the category of phenomena selected. Since all the categories taken together cover the entire range of phenomena, these "systematic sciences" extend over the entire field of knowledge. Yet they do not tell us all we need to know; for each has taken out of the actual complex of reality particular phenomena on which its interest is concentrated. If we merely add up all their findings we have not restored the original integration of the multitudinous variety of phenomena that are interrelated at any one place and time to form the living reality of that place and time.

A second approach to specialization in knowledge, therefore, is to concentrate on the variation of phenomena through time and the connections among those phenomena through time— either keeping place constant or as far as possible minimizing differences in place. During the relatively short period of record- ed history the phenomena that have changed most in character are those of society. The phenomena of physics, chemistry, botany, zoology, and physical anthropology have changed but little. Hence what we commonly call history is largely limited to the study of differences in the complex interrelations of phe- nomena which, when studied in separate categories, form also the material of the systematic social sciences. In this sense one can accept the argument that history studies everything that is studied in the social studies. It does not follow, however, that one can learn by a study of history all that may be learned in the systematic social sciences or that these could replace the need for history.

History, even human history, cannot ignore all changes in nature, since some natural conditions have changed significantly in human time. A knowledge of changes in the coast line of Holland, or in the life-habits of the fish of the North Sea, is necessary to the study of the history of the Netherlands. In the fullest sense, however, history is not limited to the life of man. Students concerned with the far longer periods involved in the history of life on the earth, or with the whole history of the earth and the universe, find themselves primarily concerned with differences and relations through time of phenomena commonly classified in the natural sciences.

It may be noted in passing that the actual division of labor in the study of these several chronological fields is not based on that logical relationship but on the training requirements dictated by the means of obtaining knowledge within them. Since the social phenomena whose relationships form the most significant changes during the most recent period of earth history are record- ed in documents of literate man, the study of this period depends primarily, though not exclusively, on competence in the study of written documents. For an earlier period the student must be specially trained to reconstruct the social phenomena that existed then out of the physical objects men used and left behind them—that is, a student of anthropology and archaeology. For prehuman history, including the vast story of the evolution of life forms, and the history of the earth itself, the records are to be read from the rocks of the earth's crust, so that the historian of that far longer period must be a particular kind of geologist, a paleontologist.

If the relation of phenomena in time were purely one of sequence without consequence, or of contemporaneousness without interrelation, history would be little more than a convenient method of cataloguing facts. Analysis of the interrelations of diverse phenomena in any period and of causal relations of development through time requires something more than mere narrative. Whether one is dealing with human history, the history of prehuman life, or the history of the earth, the scholar is expected to do more than tell the story; he must attempt to provide scientific description (as defined in the previous chapter).

If we consider the chronological sciences to include the history of every part of the earth and the universe, then in total they also extend theoretically, like the total of the systematic sciences, over the whole field of knowledge.

Even at any one time, such as the present, the different parts of the universe differ notably in phenomena association and in relations of phenomena through space. Hence, though these are ignored neither in the systematic sciences nor in the chronological sciences, there is a need for a third approach to the division of knowledge, whose primary purpose is to examine the different regions of the universe to determine their character and spatial relations.

From the earliest speculations of man concerning the universe, space appeared to consist of two entirely separate parts: the zone of mixed solid, liquid, and gaseous matter, which forms the extraordinarily varied world that is both the home of man and the only space in which he can observe directly the marvelous variety of living matter; and the nearly empty sky above, presenting the varied movements of the heavenly bodies. With the realization of the fact that the earth or world as known to man was but the outer shell of one of the minor planets in the solar system of one of the lesser stars in one of innumerable galaxies, geography and astronomy seemed logically joined in one cosmography. But both the means of observation and the purpose of study remained essentially different and separate. Geography continued to study the minutely varying surface of the earth as significant to man, while astronomy studied the celestial objects, including the planet earth, primarily as physical and chemical bodies independent of significance to man. When it became possible to study the interior of the earth by means other than those of the astronomer, there developed, as a third chorological science, the physics of the earth as a total body—geophysics.[1]

We do not find, and should not expect, clearly defined limits between the parts of space studied by the three disciplines. Geography, studying the very thin shell between earth and heaven, is dependent on the results of studies of both the other space sciences, as far as those relate to that very minute part of total space. While we have had occasion to note certain logical similarities among the sciences, notably between geography and astronomy, the great differences in the nature and distribution of the materials studied, and consequently in the purposes of study, are of greater effect in determining differences in methods of study and in accomplishments.

Whereas the causal connections in history have always been recognized by philosophers of knowledge, and the importance of physical laws in the study of planetary movements appeared to have established astronomy as a science, the need for a chorological science of the earth surface was not so clearly apparent. If the diverse phenomena found together at the same place were independent of each other in character and the relations of objects in different places had no consequences, geography would be only an encyclopedia of the phenomena to be found in different areas—as was indeed the case of many geographies published in earlier centuries. The need for specific disciplines in the study of each of the three portions of space results from the same condi-

[1] Hettner's treatment of 1905, as followed in *The Nature of Geography* [*1*:140–42], recognized but two spatial sciences, geography and astronomy, including in the latter the study of the earth as a planet. This, in effect, left no place for the study of the space represented by the interior of the earth, which indeed has only recently been "explored" by modern science.

tions—the causal relationships existing in the complex of heterogeneous phenomena at one place and the causal connections among phenomena at different places.

The almost unlimited variety of phenomena that are interrelated in the earth surface, and that can be observed and described by man, causes this small portion of space to offer the most complex area of study of any known portion of the universe. It is also the portion of the universe that is of most concern to us. To include in a single field the great variety of incommensurable phenomena that form the total complex, there must inevitably be some principle of selection. This principle is provided in geography by its concern from its earliest beginnings with the earth as the home of man. The measurement of relative importance among the unlimited variety of phenomena presented in the earth surface is determined in geography by their significance, actual or potential, direct or indirect, to man. Since that significance changes with developments in man's culture and technology, the geography of even uninhabited areas where natural conditions change little is subject to changes in time and must be re-evaluated in light of those changes.[2]

While the study of the character and interrelations of sections of space is primarily concerned with the present (or as near to the present as can be observed), it is also concerned with the character and interconnections of sections of space in past times and with the development to the present. Hence the chorological approach to knowledge of the universe also extends theoretically over the whole of empirical knowledge.

COMPARISON AND RELATIONS OF GEOGRAPHY WITH OTHER FIELDS

In this view of the three overlapping approaches to a knowledge of the universe, geography clearly is not unique. With astronomy and geophysics it is one of the chorological sciences, as history, prehistory, paleontology, etc., form the chronological sciences. These two groups are both in contrast to the systematic sciences in that they study segments of space or time in terms of whatever may be their contents, whereas the systematic sciences concentrate

[2] This paragraph, based on the discussion in Chapter V, represents an addition to, if not an alteration of, Hettner's statement.

on particular categories of objects or phenomena wherever they may be in space or time.[3]

As an aid in understanding the nature of geography, the value of this distinction among the three approaches to knowledge of reality is not challenged by the fact that we do not find complete and sharp differences. The organization of knowledge does not require a neat division into compartments, which would in fact be in violation of the essential unity of reality, but rather the recognition of coherent and manageable but preferably overlapping divisions.

Thus the student of a systematic science, primarily concerned with the characteristics and functions of a particular category of phenomena, will necessarily study those in interrelation with other phenomena, but with only incidental concern for place. In this sense, of course, every science must deal with somewhat heterogeneous phenomena, but always with the major focus on its particular category. The zoologist, as a student of a systematic science, may study the history of the animal world or the geographic distribution of different species; such studies occupy intermediate positions between the systematic and chronological sciences or between the systematic and chorological sciences.

Likewise, the student of history cannot confine his study to an area so small as to contain no significant areal differences. The history of western Europe reveals notable differences, varying through the course of time, which resulted from differences among its diverse countries. History, in short, must be in greater or less degree geographic. Conversely, as we have seen, since the concept of "the present"—or of any other point of time—is an abstraction, all geographic work must be in greater or less degree historical. The distinction between the two kinds of study is not one of separation but of difference in purpose and emphasis [cf. Darby, *68*:1–3; and Cholley, *52*:102–17].

[3] Cholley, writing in 1942, describes the distinction between geography and the systematic sciences in terms that correspond fully with the concept here presented [*52*:14]. The same is true of his statements on the comparison of geography and history, in which his phrasing corresponds very closely to that of Kant [*52*:103]. Mention may also be made of Vaumas' theoretical discussion of the place of geography among the sciences, which appears to be entirely independent of any of the other sources mentioned here but arrives at approximately similar conclusions, notably in the parallel position of history and geography [*61*].

HISTORICAL BACKGROUND OF THE CONCEPT

The concept which we have here outlined primarily on the basis of Hettner's statement was not newly created when he first published it in 1905. The germ of the idea, as we noted, was included in his first methodological article a decade earlier. Furthermore, we also know (apparently Hettner did not originally recognize this) that much the same concept had been stated in different terms a century earlier by two scholars apparently independently of each other—Kant and Humboldt [1:140].[4] Whether all three statements were in fact independently conceived or whether there was some connection from Kant to Humboldt or from either to Hettner constitutes an interesting and unresolved question in the history of geographic thought.[5] More significant than the purely biographical question is the more general question of what changes in the general thinking of geographers about their subject may account for the varying response to the concept at different periods in the development of the field. Thus the concept appears to have been unnoticed during the latter half of the nineteenth century, when geography tended to split between physical geography, pursued as a group of systematic sciences, and regional human geography. But with the restoration of the concept of geography as the study of areal variation of the earth surface following Richthofen, there was again need for recognition of the chorological approach [21].

RELATION OF THE CONCEPT TO THE PREVIOUS QUESTIONS ABOUT GEOGRAPHY

The particular characteristics of geography as a field of study, which are discussed in the earlier chapters of this monograph,

---

[4] Kant's statement, in essentially the form in which he had presented it in course lectures since 1775, was first published in 1803 in Rink's edition of *Kant's Physische Geographie,* and is quoted in translation, with corrections, in *The Nature of Geography* [1:134f.]. Humboldt's statement was published in 1793, in Latin, and included in the same form in the *Kosmos* [14:486f.], of which a complete English translation has been published [105:100].

[5] A number of writers have concluded from the facts presented in *The Nature of Geography* that Hettner depended heavily on the work of previous students, *post hoc ergo propter hoc.* Tatham, in presenting additional data, concluded that it was not adequate for more than conjectures [3:52f.]. My own subsequent study comes to a similar conclusion [105].

were not deduced from the particular concept of the position of geography among the sciences outlined in this last section. Rather they are empirical facts readily observed in the literature of geography throughout most of its long history. During much of that history geographers have debated among themselves over these characteristics of their subject, seldom having recourse to this concept. Many geographers, however, have been disturbed to observe certain differences in the character of geography as compared with those particular fields of science with which comparisons are most often made.

It is to such students, and perhaps only to them, that Hettner's concept is of value. Acceptance of the concept is in no way essential to geographic work. But students who cannot accept the particular characteristics empirically demonstrated as essential to geography, because they cannot understand that necessity, repeatedly attempt to change the subject to fit their view of what a science should be. The long history of such attempts demonstrates that their only effects are the personal frustration and professional unhappiness of those who try to fit a square peg into a round hole.

The concept is of value then if it provides a reasonable answer to the question, "Why is geography like this?" Throughout the discussion of several of the problems concerning the character of geography, comparisons with a variety of other fields of knowledge have been noted, including in each case various degrees of similarity and difference. If these fit logically into the system of classification presented in the concept, then those who have worried lest something was wrong with the character of geography need struggle no longer against what seemed to them to be out of line. For geography is thus seen as displaying those characteristics that are logically associated with a subject occupying its particular position within the whole realm of knowledge.

Does the hypothesis presented in this concept explain the particular characteristics of geography that were empirically determined? To demonstrate this one needs only to reverse the order of discussion of this paper. Given the hypothesis that the character of geography is to be determined by its position as one of the chorological sciences, determined like the chronological sciences by its method of study rather than by the kinds of things studied, and that among the chorological or space sciences it is concerned to study the earth surface, differentiated from place to place by interrelated elements significant to man, what characteristics would one expect?

These elements significant to man we know to be extremely varied in kind but in reality integrated into total complexes at each place on the earth; this forces on geography the study of integrations of greater complexity than in the systematic sciences, because it includes all their several complexities. We know that these diverse elements are not only interrelated in varying degree at every place but many of them are also interrelated among places over the world. Therefore, since we cannot study everything at once, we must study interrelations in limited segments of integration over large areas—topical geography—and also, to comprehend the character of each part of the earth, we must study more complex integrations in small units of area—regional geography. Finally, as in any science, we seek to secure that approach to certainty and universality of knowledge that is made possible by the construction of generic concepts and laws of interrelations among factors. But the manifold variety of different and incommensurable factors involved in many features of our object of study, the complex world of the earth surface, permits interpretation only of a part of our findings by that desired method. A great part of what cannot be explained by this method is nonetheless essential to an understanding and interpretation of areal variations from place to place. Hence we are forced to measure and, as best we can, interpret an unusually large number of unique cases.

If the hypothesis fits the facts previously determined, this, rather than its authorship or whatever appearance of logic it may present, is its strongest claim to validity.

XII.

Afterword

THE INSISTENCE throughout this essay on the principle that the essential characteristics of geography have been determined for us by its past development can be considered as binding or restrictive on our freedom of research only if one fails to observe the full expanse and depth of the field which that tradition provides. The earth shell which we study contains the entire world of man, and the areal variations in its character involves the greater part of the phenomena of man and the rest of nature. To comprehend these areal variations fully we must dip back into past relationships of the factors involved, and those whose interest so directs them may reach as far back into history as the availability of data may permit. Release from the necessity of focusing our attention on the relations between two particular groups of features, human and nonhuman, permits a wider expansion of interest and at the same time a more effective coherence of the entire field. The opportunity to develop generic studies leading to scientific principles is present in the many forms of topical geography. Likewise, the unlimited number of unique places in the world, each of which is important and intellectually significant at least to those who live there, provides an inexhaustible field for those most interested in this type of research.

We will not learn geography by discussing how to study geography. But in order to learn from each other we must understand the terms we use, and we can progress most rapidly if we can reach general agreement on what we wish to learn, that is, on the scope and function of our field.

By following the established methods of scholarship in our discussions about geography, we may expect to find, as did the German geographers at the turn of the century, that many fundamental issues can be resolved, leading to general agreement on basic questions concerning the scope and nature of geography. The resolution of such issues releases scholarly energies for substantive work. The value of such work is enhanced because the substantive work of many scholars pursuing common objectives permits the successive building up of knowledge into an organized system, ever stimulating and supporting the search for further learning. At the same time, as the German experience demonstrates, general agreement on basic questions permits a wide latitude for experimentation and development of new methodological concepts at the more advanced levels of research.

REFERENCES

GENERAL SOURCE REFERENCES

1. Hartshorne, Richard. *The Nature of Geography,* 1939, 1946. Originally published in *Annals* of the Association of American Geographers, XXIX (1939), 173–658; reprinted by the Association, and available from the Central Office, Library of Congress, Washington, D.C. Pages in roman numerals are included in editions since 1946.

2. Hettner, Alfred. *Die Geographie, ihre Geschichte, ihr Wesen und ihre Methoden.* Breslau, 1927. Contains most of the material published in earlier articles listed below.

3. Taylor, Griffith (ed.). *Geography in the Twentieth Century.* New York, 1951. Chapters by twenty-two authors.

4. James, Preston E., and Jones, Clarence F. (eds.). *American Geography: Inventory and Prospect.* Syracuse, 1954. A "cooperative effort," with chapters by twenty-seven leading authors.

WORKS PUBLISHED BEFORE 1939

(A much longer list is provided in the Bibliography of The Nature of Geography *[1])*

5. Bowman, Isaiah, *Geography in Relation to the Social Sciences.* New York, 1934.

6. Chamberlin, Thomas Chrowder. "The Methods of the Earth-Sciences," *Congress of Arts and Science,* Universal Exposition, St. Louis, 1904, ed. Howard J. Rogers. Boston, 1906, pp. 477–87.

7. Herbertson, Andrew J. "Regional Environment, Heredity and Consciousness," *Geographical Teacher,* VIII (1915), 147–53.

8. Hettner, Alfred. "Geographische Forschung und Bildung," *Geographische Zeitschrift,* I (1895), 1–19.

9. Hettner, Alfred. "Die Entwicklung der Geographie im 19. Jahrhundert," *Geographische Zeitschrift,* IV (1898), 305–20.

10. Hettner, Alfred. "Grundbegriffe und Grundsätze der physischen Geographie," *Geographische Zeitschrift,* IX (1903), 21–40, 121–39, 193–213.

11. Hettner, Alfred. "Das Wesen und die Methoden der Geographie," *Geographische Zeitschrift,* XI (1905), 545–64, 615–29, 671–86.

12. Hettner, Alfred. "Die Bedeutung der Morphologie," in "Methodische Zeit- und Streitfragen," *Geographische Zeitschrift,* XXIX (1923), 41–46.

13. Hettner, Alfred. "Gesetzmässigkeit und Zufall in der Geographie," *Geographische Zeitschrift,* XLI (1935), 2–15.

14. Humboldt, Alexander von. *Kosmos: Entwurf einer physischen Weltbeschreibung.* Vol. I. Stuttgart, 1845.

15. Kraft, Viktor. "Die Geographie als Wissenschaft," in *Enzyklopädie der Erdkunde,* Teil: *Methodenlehre der Geographie.* Leipzig, 1929, pp. 1–22.

16. Mackinder, Halford J. O. "On the Scope and Methods of Geography," *Proceedings of the Royal Geographical Society,* N.S. IX (1887), 141–60.

17. Mackinder, Halford J. O. "Modern Geography, German and English," *Geographical Journal,* VI (1895), 367–79.

18. Mackinder, Halford J. O. "The Human Habitat," *Scottish Geographical Magazine,* XLVII (1931), 321–35.

19. Martonne, Emmanuel de. "Évolution de la Géographie," in his *Traité de Géographie Physique.* Paris, 1919 and 1948, pp. 3–26.

20. Ogilvie, Alan G. "The Relations of Geology and Geography," *Geography,* XXIII (1938), 75–82.

21. Richthofen, Ferdinand Fr. von. *Aufgaben und Methoden der heutigen Geographie.* Leipzig: Akad. Antrittsrede, 1883.

22. Ritter, Carl. "Über das historische Element in der geographischen Wissenschaft," *Abhandlungen d. K. Akademie der Wissenschaft zu Berlin* (historisch-philologische Klasse), 1833. Republished in *Einleitung zur allgemeinen vergleichenden Geographie und Abhandlungen . . .,* Berlin, 1852. An English edition, edited by Gage, is not reliable in its translation.

23. Ritter, Carl. *Allgemeine Erdkunde* (posthumous publication of lectures at the University of Berlin). Berlin, 1862. An English edition, by Gage, is not reliable in its translation.

24. Sauer, Carl O. "The Morphology of Landscape," *University of California Publications in Geography*, II (1925), 19–53.

25. Sauer, Carl O. "Recent Developments in Cultural Geography," Chapter 4 of *Recent Developments in the Social Sciences*, ed. E. G. Hayes, Philadelphia, 1927.

26. Vidal de la Blache, Paul. "Le principe de la géographie générale," *Annales de Géographie*, V (1896), 129–42.

27. Vidal de la Blache, Paul. "Des caractères distinctifs de la géographie," *Annales de Géographie*, XXII (1913), 289–99.

28. Vidal de la Blache, Paul. *Principes de géographie humaine*. Paris, 1922. Translated as *Principles of Human Geography*, New York, 1925.

METHODOLOGICAL STUDIES PUBLISHED SINCE 1939

Geography in the German Language Area

29. Bobek, Hans, and Schmithüsen, J. "Die Landschaft im logischen System der Geographie," *Erdkunde*, III (1949), 112–20.

30. Bobek, Hans. "Gedanken über das logische System der Geographie," *Mitteilungen der Geographischen Gesellschaft in Wien*, XCIX (1957), 122–45.

31. Carol, Hans. "Die Wirtschaftslandschaft und ihre kartographische Darstellung," *Geographica Helvetica*, I (1946), 246–79.

32. Carol, Hans. "Zur Diskussion um Landschaft und Geographie," *Geographica Helvetica*, XI (1956), 111–33. Repeated (more briefly) in "Grundsätzliches zum Landschaftsbegriff," *Petermanns Geographische Mitteilungen*, CI (1957), 93–97.

33. Carol, Hans, and Neef, Ernst. "Zehn Grundsätze über Geographie und Landschaft," *Petermanns Geographische Mitteilungen*, CI (1957), 97–98.

34. De Jong, G. *Het karakter van de geografische totaliteit*. Groningen, 1955.

35. De Jong, G. "Denkvormen van het geographisch Gebied in Eenheid en Verscheidenheid" (inaugural lecture, University of Amsterdam). Groningen, 1955.

36. Lautensach, Hermann. "Otto Schlüters Bedeutung für die methodische Entwicklung der Geographie," *Petermanns Geographische Mitteilungen*, XCVI (1952), 219–31.

37. Lautensach, Hermann. *Über die Begriffe Typus und Individuum in der geographischen Forschung* (Münchner Geographische Hefte 3). Regensburg. 1953. 33 pp.

38. Lautensach, Hermann. *Die geographische Formenwandel* (Colloquium Geographicum Band 3). Bonn, 1952.

39. Otremba, E. "Die Grundsätze der naturräumlichen Gliederung Deutschlands," *Erdkunde,* II (1948) 156–67.

40. Overbeck, H. "Die Entwicklung der Anthropogeographie (insbesondere in Deutschland) seit der Jahrhundertwende und ihre Bedeutung für die geschichtliche Landesforschung," *Blätter für deutsche Landesgeschichte,* 1954, pp. 182–244.

41. Plewe, Ernst. "Vom Wesen und den Methoden der regionalen Geographie," *Studium Generale,* V (1952), 410–21.

42. Schmithüsen, Josef. "Grundsätze für die Untersuchung und Darstellung der naturräumlichen Gliederung von Deutschland," *Berichte zur deutschen Landeskunde,* VI (1949), 8–19.

43. Schmithüsen, Josef. "Einleitung: Grundsätzliches und Methodisches," in *Handbuch der naturräumlichen Gliederung Deutschlands,* Lief. 1. Remagen, 1953.

44. Schmitthenner, H. "Zum Problem der Allgemeinen Geographie," *Geographica Helvetica,* VI (1951), 123–36.

45. Schmitthenner, H. *Zum Problem der Allgemeinen Geographie und der Länderkunde* (Münchner Geographische Hefte 4). Regensburg, 1954. 37 pp.

45a. Schmitthenner, H. *Studien zur Lehre vom geographischen Formenwandel* (Münchner Geographische Hefte 7). Regensburg, 1954. 45 pp.

46. Sölch, Johann. "Die wissenschaftliche Aufgabe der modernen Geographie," *Almanach der Oesterreichischen Akademie der Wissenschaften,* XCVIII (1949), 143–62.

47. Troll, Carl. "Die geographische Landschaft und ihre Erforschung," *Studium Generale,* III (1950), 163–81.

48. Uhlig, Harald. *Die Kulturlandschaft: Methoden der Forschung und das Beispiel Nordostengland.* Kölner Geographische Arbeiten, 1956, pp. 1–98.

French Geography

49. Allix, André. "L'esprit et les méthodes de la géographie," *Études Rhodaniennes* (Université de Lyon), IV (1948), 295–310.

50. Baulig, H. "La géographie est-elle une science?" *Annales de Géographie,* LVII (1948), 1–11.

51. Chabot, G. "Les conceptions françaises de la Science géographique," *Norsk Geografisk Tidsskrift,* XII (1950), 309–21.

52. Cholley, André. *Guide de l'Étudiant en Géographie.* Paris: Presses Universitaires de France, 1942.

53. Cholley, André. "Géographie et Sociologie," *Cahiers Internationaux de Sociologie,* V (1948), 3–20.

54. Deffontaines, P. "Défense et illustration de la géographie humaine," *Revue de Géographie humaine et d'Ethnologie,* I (1948), 5–13.

55. Demangeon, Albert. "Une définition de la Géographie Humaine," in his *Problèmes de Géographie Humaine.* Paris, 1942, pp. 25–34.

56. Gottmann, Jean. "De la méthode d'analyse en géographie humaine," *Annales de Géographie,* LVI (1947), 1–12.

57. Hamelin, Edm. "La Géographie 'Difficile,'" *Cahiers de Géographie* (Université Laval, Québec), II (1952). 20 pp.

58. Le Lannou, Maurice. "Le vocation actuelle de la géographie humaine," *Études Rhodaniennes,* IV (1948), 272–80.

59. Le Lannou, Maurice. *La géographie humaine.* Paris, 1949.

60. Sorre, Max. *Les Fondements de la géographie humaine.* 3 vols. Paris, 1947–48.

61. Vaumas, Étienne de. "La Géographie. Essai sur sa nature et sa place parmi les sciences," *Revue de Géographie Alpine,* XXXIV (1946), 555–70.

British Geography

62. Baker, J. N. L. "The Geography of Bernard Varenius," *Transactions and Papers,* Institute of British Geographers, XXI (1955), 51–60.

63. Buchanan, Keith. "Geography and Human Affairs" (inaugural lecture, Victoria University College). Wellington, New Zealand, 1954.

64. Buchanan, R. O. "Approach to Economic Geography," *Indian Geographical Society, Silver Jubilee Souvenir,* 1952, pp. 1–8.

65. Clark, K. G. T. "Certain Underpinnings of our Arguments in Human Geography," *Transactions and Papers,* Institute of British Geographers, XVI (1950), 15–22.

66. Cumberland, Kenneth B. "The Geographer's Point of View" (inaugural lecture, Auckland University College). Auckland, New Zealand, 1946.

67. Darby, H. C. "Theory and Practice of Geography" (inaugural lecture, University of Liverpool). Liverpool, 1946.

68. Darby, H. C. "On the Relations of Geography and History," *Transactions and Papers,* Institute of British Geographers, XIX (1953), 1–11. Republished in 1957 ed. of *3,* pp. 640–52.

69. Edwards, K. C. "Land, Area, and Region" (inaugural lecture, University of Nottingham, 1950). Republished in *Indian Geographical Society, Silver Jubilee Souvenir,* 1952, pp. 86–96.

70. Fisher, C. A. "Economic Geography in a Changing World," *Transactions and Papers,* Institute of British Geographers, XIV (1948), 70–85.

71. Fitzgerald, Walter. Four short papers on methods and concepts of geography in *Nature,* CLII (1943), 589–93, 740–44; CLIII (1944), 481–87; CLV (1945), 355–59.

72. Forde, C. Daryll. "Human Geography, History and Sociology," *Scottish Geographical Magazine,* LV (1939), 217–35.

73. Garnier, B. J. "The Contribution of Geography" (inaugural lecture, Ibadan University College). Ibadan, Nigeria, 1952.

74. Jones, Emrys. "Cause and Effect in Human Geography," *Annals,* Association of American Geographers, XLVI (1956), 369–77.

75. Kimble, George H. T. "The Inadequacy of the Regional Concept," *London Essays in Geography.* Cambridge, 1951, pp. 151–74.

76. Kinvig, R. K. "The Geographer as Humanist," *The Advancement of Science* (British Association), XXXVIII (1953), 157–68.

77. Kirk, W. "Historical Geography and the Behavioural Environment," *Indian Geographical Society, Silver Jubilee Souvenir,* 1952, pp. 152–60.

78. Linton, David L. "Discovery, Education and Research" (inaugural lecture, University of Sheffield). Sheffield, 1946.

79. Linton, David L. *Geography and Air Photographs.* Manchester: Geographical Association, 1947.

80. Mackinder, Halford J. O. "Geography, an Art and a Philosophy," *Geography,* XXVII (1942), 122–30.

81. Manley, Gordon. "Degrees of Freedom" (inaugural lecture, Bedford College). London, 1950.

82. Martin, A. F. "The Necessity for Determinism: A Metaphysical Problem Confronting Geographers," *Transactions and Papers,* Institute of British Geographers, XVII (1951), 1–12.

83. Monkhouse, F. J. "The Concept and Content of Modern Geography" (inaugural lecture, University of Southampton). Southampton, 1955.

84. Montefiore, H. C., and Williams, W. W. "Determinism and Possibilism," *Geographical Studies* (London), II (1955), 1–11.

85. Pye, Norman. "Object and Method in Geographical Studies" (inaugural lecture, University College of Leicester). Leicester, 1955.

86. Robinson, G. W. S. "The Geographical Region: Form and Function," *Scottish Geographical Magazine,* LXIX (1953), 49–58.

87. Spate, O. H. K. "Toynbee and Huntington: A Study of Determinism," *Geographical Journal,* CXVIII (1952), 406–28 (with discussion by E. G. R. Taylor and others).

88. Spate, O. H. K. "Reflections on Toynbee's 'A Study of History,'" *Historical Studies—Australia and New Zealand,* V (1953), 324–27.

89. Spate, O. H. K. "The Compass of Geography" (inaugural lecture, Australian National University). Canberra, 1953.

90. Unstead, J. F. "Sir Halford Mackinder and the New Geography," *Geographical Journal,* CXIII (1949), 47–57.

91. Wilcock, A. W. "Region and Period," *The Australian Geographer,* VI (May, 1954). 2 pp.

92. Wooldridge, S. W. *The Geographer as Scientist.* London, 1956. Includes six methodological papers, presented between 1945 and 1954, and ten substantive papers, 1930–1954, previously published separately.

93. Wooldridge, S. W., and East, W. Gordon. *The Spirit and Purpose of Geography.* London, 1951.

94. Cumberland, K. B., *et al.* "American Geography: Review and Commentary," *New Zealand Geographer,* XI (1955), 183–94.

American Geography

95. Ackerman, Edward A. "Geographic Training, Wartime Research and Immediate Professional Objectives," *Annals,* Association of American Geographers, XXXV (1945), 121–43.

96. Ackerman, Edward A. *Geography as a Fundamental Research Discipline* (University of Chicago, Department of Geography Research Paper No. 53). Chicago, 1956. 37 pp.

97. Anderson, Robert. "Some Relations of Geography and Cultural Anthropology," *Florida Anthropologist,* IV (1953), 129–37.

98. Brooks, Charles F. "The Climatic Record: Its Content, Limitations, and Geographic Value," *Annals,* Association of American Geographers, XXXVIII (1948), 153–68.

99. Bryan, Kirk. "Physical Geography in the Training of the Geographer," *Annals,* Association of American Geographers, XXXIV (1944), 183–89.

100. Bryan, Kirk. "The Place of Geomorphology in the Geographic Sciences," *Annals,* Association of American Geographers, XL (1950), 196–208.

101. Cline, Marlin G. "Basic Principles of Soil Classification," *Soil Science,* LXVII (1949), 81–91.

102. Hartshorne, Richard. "On the Mores of Methodological Discussion in American Geography," *Annals,* Association of American Geographers, XXXVIII (1948), 113–25.

103. Hartshorne, Richard. "The Functional Approach in Political Geography," *Annals,* Association of American Geographers, XL (1950), 95–130.

104. Hartshorne, Richard. " 'Exceptionalism in Geography' Re-examined," *Annals,* Association of American Geographers, XLV (1955), 205–44.

105. Hartshorne, Richard. "The Concept of Geography as a Science of Space, from Kant and Humboldt to Hettner," *Annals,* Association of American Geographers, XLVIII (1958), 97–108.

106. James, Preston E. "Toward A Further Understanding of the Regional Concept," *Annals,* Association of American Geographers, XLII (1952), 195–222.

107. Kesseli, John E. "Geomorphic Landscapes," *Yearbook,* Association of Pacific Geographers, XII (1950), 3–10.

108. Leighly, John. "What has Happened to Physical Geography?" *Annals,* Association of American Geographers, XLV (1955), 309–18.

109. Philbrick, Allen K. "Principles of Areal Functional Organization in Regional Human Geography," *Economic Geography,* XXXIII (1957), 299–336.

109a. Philbrick, Allen K. "Areal Functional Organization in Geography," *Papers and Proceedings of the Regional Science Association,* III (1957), 87–98.

110. Platt, Robert S. "Environmentalism versus Geography," *American Journal of Sociology,* LIII (1948), 351–58.

111. Platt, Robert S. "Determinism in Geography," *Annals,* Association of American Geographers, XXXVIII (1948), 126–32.

112. Platt, Robert S. "A Review of Regional Geography," *Annals,* Association of American Geographers, XLVII (1957), 187–90.

113. Raup, Hugh M. "Trends in the Development of Geographic Botany," *Annals,* Association of American Geographers, XXXII (1942), 319–54.

114. Russell, Richard Joel. "Geographical Geomorphology," *Annals,* Association of American Geographers, XXXIX (1949), 1–11.

115. Sauer, Carl O. "Foreword to Historical Geography," *Annals,* Association of American Geographers, XXXI (1941), 1–24.

116. Schaefer, Fred K. "Exceptionalism in Geography: A Methodological Examination," *Annals,* Association of American Geographers, XLIII (1953), 226–49.

193

References

117. Sprout, Harold, and Sprout, Margaret. *Man-Milieu Relationship Hypotheses in the Context of International Politics* (Center of International Studies, Princeton University). Princeton, 1956.

118. Thornthwaite, C. W. "An Approach Toward a Rational Classification of Climate," *Geographical Review,* XXXVIII (1948), 55–94.

119. Trewartha, Glenn T. "A Case for Population Geography," *Annals,* Association of American Geographers, XLIII (1953), 71–97.

120. Ullman, Edward L. "Rivers as Regional Bonds: The Columbia-Snake Example," *Geographical Review,* XLI (1951), 210–25.

121. Ullman, Edward L. "Human Geography and Area Research," *Annals,* Association of American Geographers, XLIII (1953), 54–66.

122. Ullman, Edward L. "Geography as Spatial Interaction" (abstract), *Annals,* Association of American Geographers, XLIV (1954), 283f.

123. Ullman, Edward L. "Regional Structure and Arrangement" (mimeograph). Office of Naval Research, Contract No. Nonr–477(03), Report No. 10, Dec. 1954. University of Washington, Seattle.

124. Van Cleef, Eugene. "Areal Differentiation and the 'Science' of Geography," *Science,* CXV (June 13, 1953), 654–55.

125. Van Cleef, Eugene. "Must Geographers Apologize?" *Annals,* Association of American Geographers, XLV (1955), 105–08.

126. Whittlesey, Derwent. "The Horizon of Geography," *Annals,* Association of American Geographers, XXXV (1945), 1–36.

Others

127. Grigorief, A. A. "Geography in the Capitalist Countries in the Epoch of Imperialism," *Great Soviet Encyclopedia,* Vol. X (1954), pp. 464ff. A translation, by a graduate student at the University of Wisconsin, is available.

128. Kalliola, Reino. "Eräitä maantieteen metodologisia peruskysmuksiä," *Eripainos Terrasta,* N:o 2, 1956, pp. 40–50. Abstract in German.

129. Stevens-Middleton, Rayfred Lionel. *La Obra de Alexander von Humboldt en Mexico, Fundamento de la Geografía Moderna.* Publ. No. 202, Instituto Panamericano de Geografía e Historia, México, D.F., 1956. Abstract in *Annals,* Association of American Geographers, XLV (1955), 297.

130. Massip y Valdés, Salvador. *La Geografía y su importancia en la resolución de los problemas planteados a la nación cubana* (inaugural lecture, University of Havana). Havana, 1951.

131. Zarur, Jorge. *Precisão e Applicabilidade na Geografia.* Rio de Janeiro, 1955.

AUTHOR INDEX

Ackerman, Edward A., 122, 127, 160–61, 191

Allix, André, 46, 50, 52, 57, 65, 67, 73, 157, 188

Anderson, Robert, 33, 169, 191

Bain, Alexander, 116

Baker, J. N. L., 109, 189

Baulig, H., 167, 188

Berger, Ernst Hugo, 108

Bobek, Hans, 74, 121, 122, 125, 142, 187

Bowman, Isaiah, 27, 152, 165, 167, 168–69, 185

Braun, Gustav, 9

Brooks, Charles F., 97, 98, 191

Bryan, Kirk, 69, 87, 191

Buchanan, Keith, 189

Buchanan, R. O., 189

Bucher, August Leopold, 31

Carol, Hans, 24–25, 42, 74, 131, 134, 136, 142, 187

Chabot, G., 167, 188

Chamberlin, Thomas C., 154–56, 167, 185

Cholley, André, 14, 21, 30, 37, 44–45, 71, 81, 86, 100, 110, 112, 141, 160, 179, 180, 189

Clark, Andrew, 101, 103, 185(#4)

Clark, K. G. T., 55, 189

Cline, Martin G., 92, 191

Cumberland, Kenneth B., 103, 189, 191

Darby, H. C., 7, 15, 99, 102, 180, 189

Davis, William Morris, 35, 70, 106

Deffontaines, P., 42, 189

De Jong, G., 36, 54, 111, 126, 127, 133, 134, 136, 140, 141, 187

Demangeon, Albert, 189

Dickinson, Robert E., 134

East, W. Gordon, 20, 43, 56, 62, 68–69, 90, 92, 93, 106, 191

Edwards, K. C., 67, 190

Fairgrieve, James, 68

Fawcett, C. B., 134

Febvre, Julien, 56

Fisher, C. A., 55, 190

Fitzgerald, Walter, 190

Fleure, H. J., 69

Forde, C. Daryl, 55, 86, 190

Garnier, B. J., 55, 190

Gerland, George, 29, 110

Glossary Committee, 14, 23

Gottman, Jean, 53, 189

Gottschalk, Louis, 166, 167

Gradmann, Robert, 38

Grigorief, A. A., 193

Hamelin, Edm., 4, 23, 32, 167, 189

Hammond, Edward, 89

Hartshorne, Charles, 155

Hartshorne, Richard (exclusive of references to #1), 2, 7, 14, 31, 72, 93, 180, 185(#4), 192

Herbertson, Andrew J., 5, 42, 51, 67, 186

Hettner, Alfred, 3, 10, 12–14, 17, 20, 23, 24, 37–43, 46, 50, 62, 66–67, 80, 81, 87, 94, 99, 101, 102, 110–12, 122, 123, 128, 129, 131, 134, 136, 153, 154, 160, 168, 173–80, 185, 186

Humboldt, Alexander von, 4, 12, 20, 22, 28–30, 34–35, 48, 64, 67–68, 70–73, 109, 147, 151, 162, 180, 186

James, Preston E., 14, 67, 129, 185(#4), 192
James, William, 154
Johnson, Douglas, 87
Jones, Emrys, 99, 154, 190
Jones, Stephen B., 36
Jones, Wellington D., 134

Kalliola, Reino, 20, 193
Kant, Immanuel, 22, 25, 67, 109, 180
Kesseli, John E., 91, 93, 96, 192
Kimble, George H. T., 190
Kinvig, R. K., 23–24, 190
Kirk, W., 58, 190
Koeppen, Wladimir P., 124
Kraft, Viktor, 30, 41, 186

Lautensach, Hermann, 3, 39, 41, 110, 128, 136, 142, 151, 187–88
Lehmann, Otto, 25, 112, 154
Leighly, John, 70, 94, 98, 185(#4), 192
Le Lannou, Maurice, 44, 53, 55, 57, 71, 86, 96, 99, 110, 113, 151, 189
Linton, David L., 23, 58, 91, 167, 190

Mackinder, Halford J. O., 5, 24, 27, 31, 68, 99, 101, 110, 186, 190, 191
Manley, Gordon, 3, 4, 190
Marthe, Friedrich, 28
Martin, A. F., 59, 190
Martonne, Emmanuel de, 186
Massip y Valdes, Salvador, 193

Michotte, P., 55, 112
Monkhouse, F. J., 103, 190
Montefiore, H. C., 57, 63, 154–56, 166, 190

Neef, Ernst, 187

Obst, Erich, 9, 128
Ogilvie, Alan G., 87, 186
Otremba, E., 74, 75, 188
Overbeck, H., 134, 188

Passarge, Siegfried, 124
Peltier, Louis C., 92, 185(#4)
Penck, Albrecht, 90, 112
Peschel, Oscar, 28
Philbrick, Allen K., 135, 137, 192
Platt, Robert S., 55, 64, 70, 134, 135, 154, 155, 165, 171, 192
Pleve, Ernst, 12, 40, 41, 45, 188
Prunty, Merle C., 52
Pye, Norman, 190

Radcliffe-Brown, Alfred R., 170–71
Ratzel, Friedrich, 4, 19, 28, 56–58
Raup, Hugh, 20, 192
Richthofen, Ferdinand Frh. von, 2, 12, 23–24, 29–30, 110, 112, 173, 180, 186
Rickert, Heinrich, 148
Ritter, Carl, 4, 12, 19, 22, 24, 28, 29, 37, 43–44, 48, 60, 62, 65, 73, 83, 109, 116, 128, 146, 186
Robinson, Arthur H., 162
Robinson, G. W. S., 134, 190
Russell, Richard Joel, 84–85, 91, 93, 96, 192

Sauer, Carl, 12, 15, 17, 43, 55, 60, 67, 102, 187, 192
Schaefer, Fred K., 2, 31, 192
Schlüter, Otto, 39, 41, 65, 80, 187
Schmidt, Peter Heinrich, 112

Schmithüsen, Josef, 42, 74–75, 142, 188

Schmitthenner, Heinrich, 3, 19, 45, 110, 128, 142, 188

Semple, Ellen C., 56–58

Sidaritsch, Marian, 134

Smailes, A. E., 134

Sölch, Johann, 12, 188

Sorre, Max, 189

Spate, O. H. K., 18, 42, 43, 56, 58, 60, 62, 104, 191

Sprout, Harold and Margaret, 52, 55, 57, 58–59, 62, 193

Spuhler, James, 169

Stevens, Rayfred L. Middleton, 29, 147, 193

Strabo, 15

Tatham, George, 48, 57, 58, 62, 68, 180, 185(#3)

Taylor, E. G. R., 55, 58

Taylor, Griffith, 58, 62, 185(#3)

Thornthwaite, C. Warren, 124, 193

Trewartha, Glenn T., 53, 193

Troll, Karl, 24, 142, 188

Uhlig, Harald, 37, 74, 135, 142, 188

Ullman, Edward L., 19, 71, 88, 91, 134, 135, 185(#4), 193

Unstead, J. F., 5, 191

Vallaux, Camille, 35

Van Cleef, Eugene, 128, 146, 193

Varen (Varenius), Bernard, 42, 67, 108–09, 189

Vaumas, Étienne de, 179, 189

Vidal de la Blache, Paul, 13, 15, 24, 30, 32, 56, 67, 108–09, 116, 187

Volz, Wilhelm, 15

Wagner, Hermann, 2, 29, 110, 147–48

Watson, J. Wreford, 32, 185(#3)

Whittlesey, Derwent, 67, 102, 131, 134, 139, 185(#4), 193

Wilcock, A. W., 127, 191

William-Olsson, William, 171

Williams, W. W., 57, 63, 154–56, 166, 190

Windelband, Wilhelm, 148

Wooldridge, S. W., 5, 6, 20, 43, 45, 56, 58, 62, 65, 68–69, 82, 85, 87, 90–95, 106, 185(#3), 191

Zarur, Jorge, 193

SUBJECT INDEX

agriculture, 72, 77, 132
American College Dictionary, 14, 18, 93
appearance of areas, 41, 42
areal differentiation, 12–21, 62
areal variation, 17, 21, 118–20, 126, 159, 183
"areas of certain type," 133
astronomy, 22, 35, 116–17, 142, 150, 157, 177, 178

biogeography, 68–69
biology, 150, 157
botany, 20, 142–43

causes, 13, 18–19, 87–88, 99, 165, 170; *see also* process relations
change, 83, 85–86, 96, 98
character of areas, 13, 30, 41, 116, 131, 137
chorological sciences, 176–79, 181–82
chorology, 13, 30
chronological sciences, 175–76, 178, 179, 181–82
circulation, geography of, 72
city, 72
classification, 78, 91–93; *see also* types
classification, inorganic, organic, and social, 30, 33–34, 74–75, 119, 123–26
climate, 66, 73, 77, 78, 96–98, 120, 123, 132, 133, 140
climatology, 97
coal, 89–90
combinations of phenomena, 14, 30; *see also* interrelations
compage, 139–40

comparative regional geography, 163–65
consumption, geography of, 73, 77
cosmography, 22
cultural factor, 51–52
cultural heritage, 120, 140, 152, 159
cultural landscape, 49–50

deltas, 84–85, 93
demography, 150
description, 13, 17, 89–91, 97, 99, 102, 116, 170–72
determinism, scientific, 153–57, 168; *see also* geographical determinism *and* environmentalism
distance, 117, 141
distributions, 112, 133
dualism: physical and human geography, 65–80; regional and systematic geography, 108–45
dynamic *vs.* static, 81–82, 83, 99, 135

earth shell, 24–25, 46, 69–70
earth surface, 22–25, 176, 178
economic geography, 72–73
economics, 150
element-complex, 74, 123–27
environment, 52, 61; *see also* natural environment *and* nonhuman environment
environmentalism, 39–40, 43, 54–64, 70
Erdkunde, 23
exchange, geography of, 73

fishing, 77
formal regions, 131–45

fossils, 40
freedom of will, 126, 153–56
functional regions, 134–45
fundamental research, 160–61

general geography, 108–11; *see also* systematic geography
generalization, defined, 136
generic concepts, 16–17, 37, 101, 120–21, 132, 138, 182, 183
generic regions, 132–33, 137, 144
genesis in geography, 84, 86–94, 97, 99–102, 162–65
genetic classification, 91–93
"geographical conditions," 56
geographical determinism, 56–64
"geographic factor," 62
geographic history, 101
geography: defined, 13–14, 21, 47, 172; in antiquity, 108; in British areas, 4–6, 55–56; in French-speaking areas, 4, 30, 56–57, 71; in German-speaking areas, 2–4, 29–30, 55, 74–75, 109–10, 184; in secondary schools, 80; in United States, 5–6, 55–56
geology, 86–95, 150, 157; *see also* historical geology *and* paleontology
geomorphology, 75, 84–96; *see also* landforms
geophysics, 177, 178
geosphere, 24

heterogeneity, 26–35, 66, 80, 151
hierarchy of regions, 132, 137
historical geography, 84, 101–07
historical geology, 34, 81, 86, 94, 142, 173, 176, 178
history, 34, 35, 84, 100, 103, 142, 145, 148, 159, 167, 173, 175–76, 177, 179; in geography, 81, 98–107, 183
"home of man," 22, 42, 45–47, 69, 105, 176, 178
homogeneity, 130–36
horizontal unity, 134

human factors, 48–64; *see also* classification, inorganic, organic, and social
human geography, 28, 31, 65–67, 71–73
hydrosphere, 24

ice areas, 79
idiographic, 149
individual cases, 37, 115–16, 128–29, 132, 136–37, 182; *see also* places
individual persons, 126, 152
inorganic; *see* classification, inorganic, organic, and social
integration, in geography, 32–35, 74–80, 123, 125–27, 133, 137–45, 174, 182
intelligence work, 143
interconnections of places, 13, 19, 37–41, 46, 113–31, 134–41, 159, 178, 182
interrelations, 13, 17–19, 28, 30, 34, 37–41, 46, 49–50, 80, 83, 99–100, 102, 104, 113–41, 177, 182

landforms, 66, 77, 84–96, 129, 140
land holdings, 52, 77
landscape, 23, 25, 31, 41, 49
Landschaft, 3–4, 23, 25, 31, 110, 142
Landschaftsbild, 23, 41
Landschaftskunde, 37
land tenure, 77
laws: in science, 28, 60, 63, 70, 79–80, 94, 109, 120, 146–72, 182; concerning regions, 148, 160
location, 117, 130, 141, 159

magnetic declination, 40
man: in geography, 41–47; as an integrating factor, 125–26; as a physical agent, 42
"man-land" relationships, 56; *see also* nature-man relationships
manufacturing, 72, 132
marketing geography, 73

meteorology, 77

methodological discussion, 2–9, 183–84

metropolitan regions, 134

microgeography, 128

milieu, 30, 71

mineral resources, 72, 73, 75, 76, 120, 125, 140

mosaic, 127, 129

natural environment, 43, 52, 56–59, 71

natural factors, 48–64

"natural geography," 65, 124

natural landscape, 49, 102

natural regions, 42, 43, 74–75, 125, 141

natural sciences *vs.* social sciences, 55, 61, 80

nature, 48

nature-man relationships, 18, 40, 56, 61, 62, 70, 79, 183; *see also* environmentalism

nodal regions, 134–35

nomothetic, 149

nonhuman environment, 59

oceans, 76–77, 79, 120

paleontology, 176, 178

periods of history, 145

philosophy, 79, 168

physical geography, 28, 31, 43, 65–71

physical geography *vs.* human geography, 48–80

physics, 154, 156

places, 13, 15, 116, 157–58, 183

plant geography, 20, 142–43

political science, 157

population, 53

possibilism, 56–59

prediction, 165–66

present, the, 82, 84, 96, 98–99, 101, 178–79

primeval landscape, 49

principles, scientific; *see* laws, in science

"probablism," 58–59

process relations, 32, 85, 111–12, 125, 133, 136

railroads, 52, 88

regional geography, 108–45, 147, 163, 164, 182

regional method, 129–43

regions, 129–43, 159–90 (*see also* formal, functional, generic, natural, specific, and uniform regions); as real objects, 31, 110

relationships; *see* interrelations *and* nature-man relationships

representative areas, 164

rivers, 75

rural, 77, 79

sampling, 159

science, nature of, 108–09, 112–13, 146–48, 167–72

sciences, classification of, 173–82

selection of phenomena, 36–47

sensually observable phenomena, 31, 36–37

significance, in geography, 36–47

similarity, 16–17, 130, 131

social sciences, 55, 80

sociology, 162

soils, 54, 66, 73, 76, 77, 120, 124, 132

space sciences, 176–79

spatial arrangement, 31

spatial interaction, 127; *see also* interconnections of places

species, 150–52

specific regions, 132, 136–37

static *vs.* dynamic, 81–82, 83, 135

statistical methods, 10, 161–62

systematic geography, 108–45; *see also* topical divisions in geography *and* topical studies

systematic sciences, 20, 27, 32–35, 71, 73, 79, 80, 84, 97, 101, 107, 111–12, 121, 133, 174, 178, 182 teleology, 43, 48, 62

time, in geography, 81–107

topical divisions in geography, 65–80

topical studies, 121, 129–45, 147, 163, 164, 182, 183

totality, 13, 37, 44, 46, 73–74, 114, 121, 164, 171

transportation, 72, 77

types, 78, 151, 158; of areas, 128–29, 159–60

uniform regions, 131–36

unique cases, 146, 149; *see also* individual cases

universals, 159, 160–61

urban areas, 72, 79

vegetation, 34, 66, 75, 85, 120, 124–25

"vertical unity," 134

wholes, 103, 136

wild areas, 79

wild landscape, 49

world, 25, 44, 47